Fed up with not making enough bodybuilding progress?

Ready to try a legendary routine that's proven to pack on lots of muscle mass fast?

The guidance in this book teaches Course #1. Before anabolic steroids started to infest the bodybuilding world, variations of Course #1 were famous, popular, and responsible for building tons of muscle. But in the 1960s, when the use of steroids became popular among competitive bodybuilders, the popularity of Course #1 began to wane. Since then, the routines most commonly promoted in bodybuilding publications have been those used by physique stars who were genetically gifted for bodybuilding *and* on steroids. But those routines don't work well, if at all, for most other bodybuilders.

Here are the three primary characteristics of Course #1:

1) **It's very effective.** Its track record for muscle growth is illustrious. (It's not a newfangled, bogus routine that's hyped up with pseudo science and fictitious endorsements.)

2) **It's up to date.** The routine has been modernized in this book. The version you can apply is even better than the original one. (There are better training tools available today, and knowledge of nutrition and the other components of recuperation is much greater nowadays.)

3) **It's personalized.** You'll be taught how to modify the routine so that it suits you perfectly.

When applied properly, this may be the #1 muscle-building routine for drug-free, genetically typical bodybuilders. And because this legendary routine doesn't require long or overly frequent workouts, it's suitable even for busy people.

Join in the revival of Course #1, build lots of muscle, and become a bodybuilding success story.

But be ready for training concepts that are radically different to what you're used to.

And set aside any doubts you may have.

Simply apply Course #1 as it's explained in this book, and experience the muscle-building magic yourself. Then you'll really be a believer.

D1288563

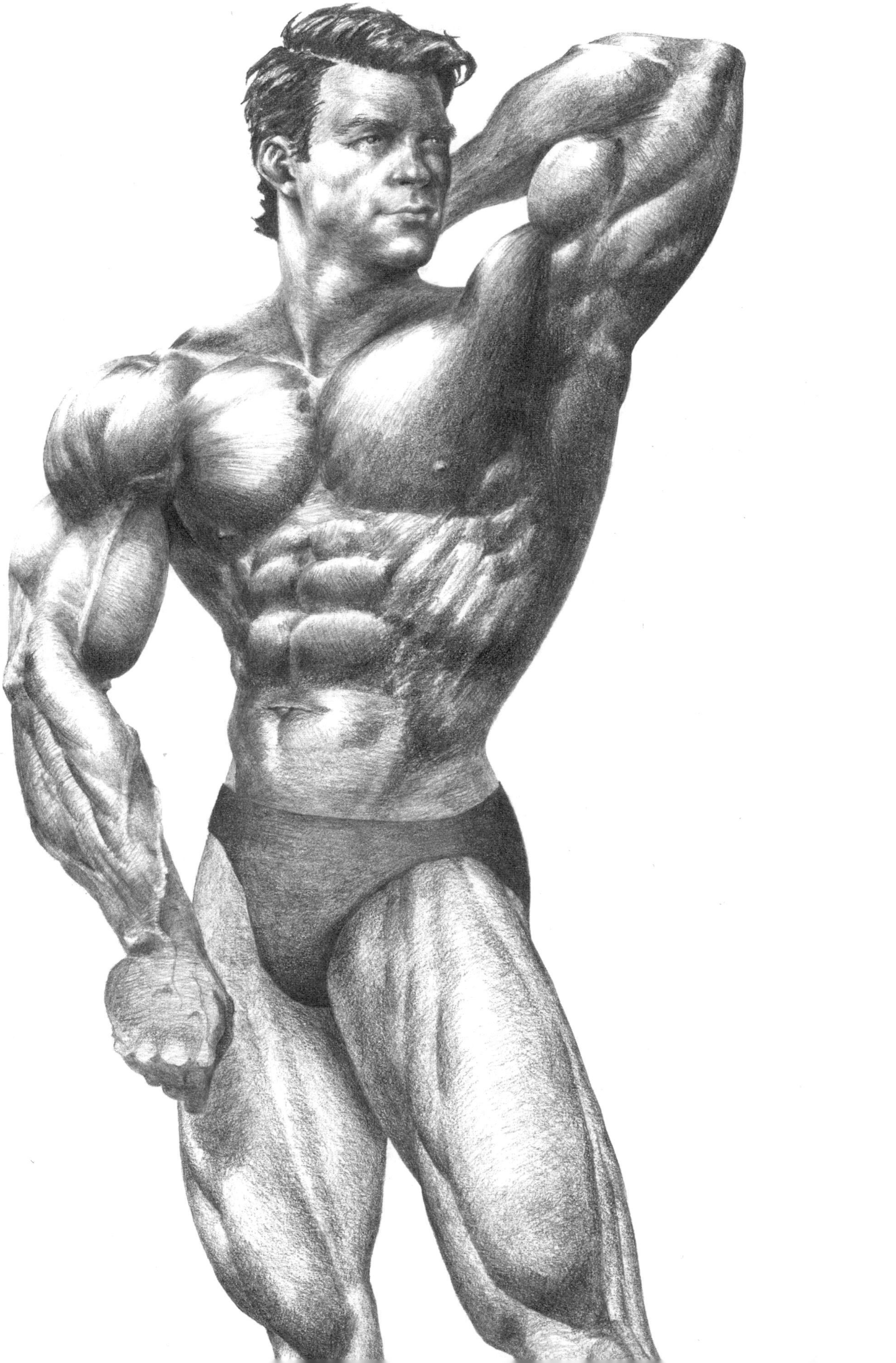

Warning . . . SAFETY

Every effort was made in this book to stress the importance of correct technique and safety measures when using exercise programs. Regardless of your age, check with your doctor to ensure that it's appropriate for you to follow such programs. Proceed with caution, and at your own risk.

Warning . . . DISCLAIMER

The purpose of this book is to provide information on bodybuilding and related topics. It's sold with the understanding that neither the publisher nor author are engaged in providing legal, medical, or other professional services. Every effort has been made to make this book as thorough and accurate as possible. Despite this, all information on the subject matter has not been included, and there may be mistakes in both content and typography.

CS Publishing, the author and distributors of this book shall have neither liability nor responsibility to any entity or person with respect to any injury, loss, or damage caused, or alleged to be caused, directly or indirectly, by the material in this book.

If you don't wish to be bound by the above, you may return your copy to the publisher for a refund.

Trademarks

All terms mentioned in this book that are known to be trademarks have been marked as such, but CS Publishing can't attest to the accuracy of this information. There may be unintentional omissions in acknowledging trademarks. The publication and use of this book doesn't affect the validity of any trademark or service mark.

Photography credits

I would like to thank the models, all of whom generously gave their time, and the gym owners, all of whom generously gave access to their premises. They were all wonderfully cooperative.

Left, Ian Duckett, owner of Body in Design Gym, Leeds, England; then Helen Everson, Jenny Garside, and Robin Gorry. All of their photos were taken at Ian's gym.

Con Demetriou. All photos of Con were taken by Mike Christofides at what was then Gold's Gym in Nicosia, Cyprus.

Eleni Papadopoulos. All photos of Eleni were taken at Olympus Gym in Nicosia, Cyprus.

Here are the credits for the other models shown in this book: Brian Carlton, pages 170 and 172; Chip Kent, page 139; and Korinna McRobert, page 90.

Stuart McRobert's

BRAWN
SERIES

BOOK 1

HOW TO BUILD UP TO 50 POUNDS OF MUSCLE THE NATURAL WAY

Stuart McRobert

Author of BRAWN, BEYOND BRAWN, and
BUILD MUSCLE, LOSE FAT, LOOK GREAT

CS Publishing Ltd., P.O. Box 20390, CY-2151 Nicosia, Cyprus
tel + 357-2233-3069   cspubltd@spidernet.com.cy   www.hardgainer.com

US office: CS Publishing Ltd., P.O. Box 1002, Connell, WA 99326
tel 509-234-0362   info@hardgainer.com   www.hardgainer.com

Printed in the United States of America.

Cyprus Library Cataloging-in-Publication Data
McRobert, Stuart, 1958–
How to build up to 50 pounds of muscle the natural way / Stuart McRobert
v.1 : photos., ill. ; cm. -- (Stuart McRobert's New BRAWN series)
Includes index
ISBN 978-9963-9991-3-2 (series)
ISBN 978-9963-9991-2-5 (v.1 : pbk)
1. Bodybuilding--Handbook, manuals, etc.   2. Bodybuilding--Training   3. Physical fitness
4. Exercise I.Title

613.713--ddc23   2012010901

Contents

1 The Revelations
Foundation understanding   *10*

2 The Procedures
The essentials of proper implementation of **Course #1**   *32*

3 The Recuperation
How to permit growth   *66*

4 The Foundation Phase
What you must do to be ready to implement *The Growth Phase*   *80*

5 The Exercise Technique
How to master the correct form of **Course #1's** exercises   *94*

6 The Growth Phase
Course #1's training schedules, and how to apply them   *176*

About the author   *204*
Index   *212*

The Revelations *itemized*

#1: Some history of how to build 50 pounds (23 kilos) of muscle   *12*

#2: Why **Course #1** will work for you   *13*

#3: The problem with conventional bodybuilding methods   *14*

#4: Why you shouldn't copy the bodybuilding champions   *15*

#5: Economics and **Course #1**   *16*

#6: Genetics   *17*

#7: Hard gainers and easy gainers   *18*

#8: Substance first, detail later   *20*

#9: The necessity of abbreviated training   *21*

#10: The magic of the barbell squat   *22*

#11: The squat alternatives   *23*

#12: The advantages of the parallel-grip deadlift   *24*

#13: The magic of 20 reps   *25*

#14: The quantity of muscle you can build   *26*

#15: The *enhanced* version in contrast with the *traditional* version   *28*

#16: Individual variation   *30*

#17: Desire, determination and dedication   *31*

Important note: The structure of **Course #1**

The Revelations (Chapter 1) summarize the essential background of **Course #1**. Then come the chapters that explain the constituent elements of **Course #1**.

The Procedures (Chapter 2) cover the nuts and bolts of training, and apply to all good training routines, not just **Course #1**.

The Recuperation (Chapter 3) explains the essentials of recovery, which apply to all routines.

The Foundation Phase (Chapter 4), which is unique to **Course #1**, teaches the requirements you must satisfy before you'll be ready to start on *The Growth Phase*.

The Exercise Technique (Chapter 5) teaches the form that's required for the **Course #1** exercises, but which also applies to other routines.

The Growth Phase (Chapter 6) teaches the special training schedules that define **Course #1**.

Only when you properly apply all the constituent elements can you realize the tremendous rewards that are possible from implementing Course #1.

The Procedures *itemized*

#1: Fully attend to the components of recuperation   *34*

#2: Be sure where you train is conducive to progress   *35*

#3: Use good machinery or no machinery at all   *36*

#4: Choose exercises that are well suited *to you*   *37*

#5: Use correct exercise technique   *38*

#6: Develop suppleness   *39*

#7: Take action to remove physical hindrances   *40*

#8: Use a controlled rep speed   *41*

#9: Train hard!   *42*

#10: Use exercise intensifiers sparingly, if at all   *43*

#11: Vary your training intensity over time   *44*

#12: Build strength   *45*

#13: Build strength over multiple set-rep formats   *46*

#14: Use accurate weight plates   *48*

#15: Use *little gems*   *49*

#16: Apply *relentless progression* and *gaining momentum*   *50*

#17: Earn your poundage increments   *51*

#18: Develop a strong grip   *52*

#19: Use recommended grip aids   *53*

#20: Keep a training logbook   *54*

#21: Get a training partner   *55*

#22: Don't wear a lifting belt   *56*

#23: Avoid excessive breath holding   *57*

#24: Wear appropriate footwear   *58*

#25: Time your workouts properly   *59*

#26: Time your pre-workout meal with care   *60*

#27: Open each workout with a general warm-up   *61*

#28: Do warm-up work specific to each exercise   *62*

#29: Keep hydrated, and have a post-workout feed   *63*

#30: Deal with sickness without harming your progress   *64*

#31: Create a *training sanctuary*   *65*

1

Never mind about the training routines that genetic supermen prosper on, especially when those genetic freaks are bolstered with bodybuilding drugs.

Those training routines are a total waste of time for most bodybuilders.

The Revelations
Foundation understanding

Get a grip on your training!

REVELATION #1
Some history of how to build 50 lbs (23 kgs) of muscle

In the early twentieth century, the pioneers who established the foundation for **Course #1** included Mark Berry, Joseph Curtis Hise, and Peary Rader. It was Peary's amazing success with a Hise-inspired, 20-rep-squat interpretation of **Course #1** that enabled him to transform his physique. Peary wanted to teach others the marvelous procedures he had learned, and he did so through *Iron Man* magazine, which he started in 1936.

After 12 years of failure on other routines, Peary gained 10 pounds in one month on **Course #1**. He then gained a little over 75 further pounds in the following two years, which gave him the foundation of muscle and strength to enable him to win the heavyweight Olympic lifting title in the mid-western division of the USA for eight years.

Here's why Peary's success is of huge importance to drug-free, genetically typical bodybuilders:

a) He struggled for many years before he finally made good progress, so he definitely wasn't genetically gifted for bodybuilding.

b) His success occurred about 20 years before anabolic steroids were first made available to athletes, so it was definitely a drug-free accomplishment.

c) Even though Peary was genetically typical and drug-free, he still had amazing success.

Peary's *Iron Man* became very influential. Although it featured the methods of genetic supermen, and since around 1960 it reported the training routines of bodybuilders who used anabolic steroids, Peary relentlessly recommended interpretations of **Course #1**. He knew that that instruction was the best for drug-free, genetically typical bodybuilders. *Iron Man* reported many success stories of readers who followed Peary's recommendations.

Iron Man continues today. Peary sold it in 1986, and John Balik became the managing partner.

Peary, 1909 to 1991, was the most important single influence on my bodybuilding education. He was also the first to publish my articles, starting in 1981, which enabled me to get a foothold in the world of bodybuilding journalism. I'm very thankful to Mr. Rader, and indebted to him.

As Charles A. Smith used to put it, "It's upon the pioneers' shoulders that we have to stand in order to be as tall as they. We're merely the heirs of those who have gone before us."

Charles worked on Joe Weider's bodybuilding magazines in the 1950s, and was one of the final links with the pioneers of bodybuilding.

Peary Rader's transformation—almost 90 pounds worth (40 kilos)—happened many years ago. But what worked for him back then can work for you right now. Human physiology hasn't changed.

REVELATION #2
Why Course #1 will work for you

No other account of how to apply Course #1 has provided the thoroughness that's presented in this book.

a) **Course #1** promoted in this book is the modernized, enhanced version of the original one. Important improvements have been made because there are better training tools and aids available today than during Peary's era, and knowledge of nutrition and the other components of recovery is much greater now. The improvements have a two-fold benefit:
    i) To increase the number of bodybuilders that can prosper on **Course #1**.
    ii) To increase the effectiveness of **Course #1** for everyone who uses it.

b) The technique of the individual exercises is explained thoroughly. You'll learn precisely how to perform each one, and thus avoid the form errors that commonly undermine progress.

c) All the details of training are explained thoroughly. You'll learn everything you must do *in the gym* in order to provide the required muscle growth stimulus.

d) All the details of recuperation are also explained thoroughly. You'll learn everything you must do *outside the gym* so that you're able to respond fully to the muscle growth stimulus.

e) Careful consideration has been given to individual variation. Variations in genetic potential for muscle growth, recovery ability, training facilities and the suitability or otherwise of certain exercises have been allowed for.

Nothing has been left to chance.

Allow Course #1 to work its magic on you.

My success story

My untrained adult bodyweight was about 135 pounds (62 kilos), at about 5-9 (175 cms). I eventually reached 195 pounds (89 kilos). Peary took about two years to make his gain of almost 90 pounds (40 kilos), but I needed a much longer period to make my gain of 60 pounds (27 kilos). My short stints of successful abbreviated training were scattered over many years. Most of that time was spent applying conventional training methods, albeit without any success whatsoever. For a drug-free, genetically typical bodybuilder, my 60-pound gain was impressive, and it transformed me. The majority of the gain was from applying variations of **Course #1**.

Most of my applications of **Course #1** used the barbell squat as the linchpin exercise. Although I'm not structurally well suited to the barbell squat, I almost made the 300 pounds (136 kilos) for 20 reps mark for praiseworthy achievement for a drug-free, genetically typical bodybuilder. (My best was 290 or 285 x 20.) But when I recognized my structural deficiencies for the barbell squat, and focused on the deadlift instead, I eventually deadlifted 400 pounds (182 kilos) for 20 reps.

REVELATION #3

The problem with conventional bodybuilding methods

Bodybuilding is a wonderful activity *provided* you get good results. But unless you have a terrific genetic inheritance for bodybuilding, or unless you're propped up with dangerous bodybuilding drugs, conventional bodybuilding routines deliver little or no muscle development.

Conventional bodybuilding methods prescribe a traditional split routine, more training days than non-training days, many isolation exercises, multiple exercises for every body part, and dozens of work sets per workout. And full-body routines of too many exercises performed too frequently are also ineffective for most bodybuilders.

   a) Conventional methods promote workout volume and frequency that are impractical for busy people and no more than minimally effective for most bodybuilders, if effective at all.

   b) Conventional methods promote high-risk exercises and dangerous techniques that have injured countless bodybuilders.

   c) Conventional methods promote exaggerated expectations, and invariably use drug-fed genetic phenomena as gurus and role models.

   d) Conventional methods aren't personalized to meet individual needs and goals.

   e) Conventional methods encourage drug assistance because without drug use those methods don't work well for most bodybuilders.

Stop following instruction that doesn't work. More of what didn't help you over the last few months isn't going to help you over the next few months.

This book focuses on the priority of most bodybuilders: how to build muscle mass. It doesn't cover the pre-contest refinement needed by competitive bodybuilders because that's relevant to just a tiny minority.

I'm just one of many bodybuilders who gave their all to conventional training methods, found them to be ineffective, but eventually came across alternative methods that work. This book isn't based on just one man's journey, but is a distillation of the experiences and acquired wisdom from generations of bodybuilders.

Course #1 and women

There's no tradition of **Course #1** being used by women, and that's reflected in the text of this book. But the book's guidance will work very well for women who apply it properly. The principles that **Course #1** is based on aren't gender specific.

But some aspects of the guidance need to be modified for women—growth expectations, exercise poundages, dietary quantities, and the body fat percentage ceiling prior to starting a cycle of **Course #1**. For the latter, while the recommendation for men is 12 to 15% body fat, a comparable figure for many women is more like 19 to 22%.

REVELATION #4

Why you shouldn't copy the bodybuilding champions

I started training in a gym in 1973, aged 15, when Arnold Schwarzenegger was in his prime as a bodybuilder. His training methods were promoted without caveats. The format was basically this: *"Here's how the champion does it. Train, eat, and take food supplements like the champion does, to become a champion yourself."*

I was obsessed with trying to build a great physique. All I wanted was to study bodybuilding, train, and apply myself to recuperating between workouts. But I couldn't distinguish between good and poor instruction. I trained as the famous bodybuilders of the time recommended. If it was in print and supposedly written by a champion bodybuilder, I believed it.

I trained harder than anyone else at the gyms I attended, I ate very well, I took lots of food supplements, and I got plenty of sleep. I epitomized dedication to bodybuilding, and couldn't understand why I didn't make great progress. For a long time I didn't make any progress. It was only many years later that I understood why:

a) I didn't have outstanding genetics for muscle-building. (I used to believe that genetics didn't matter at all.)

b) I wasn't "supplementing" with anabolic steroids. (I used to believe that the only supplements the champions took were vitamins, minerals, and protein shakes.)

The methods advocated by elite bodybuilders hindered my development—they caused overtraining, injuries, and sickness. Countless other bodybuilders have been similarly harmed. And the mayhem continues today because the sort of "instruction" that misled me and millions of others during the 1970s and 1980s is still promoted today.

Physique champions have inspired millions of bodybuilders over the years, but they have also misled millions of bodybuilders.

When I learned about bodybuilding drugs I was sensible enough not to use them. I put my health first. (Anabolic steroids produce improved recuperation and greater muscle mass, and enable those who use them to prosper on high-volume training—*but at a cost to their health.* The cost can be very serious—for example, heart and liver problems, psychiatric issues, and joint and connective tissue problems due to the abuse sustained from high-volume training.)

Train like a modern-day, superstar bodybuilder and you'll never develop a terrific physique naturally *unless* you have freaky genetics for bodybuilding.

Some famous bodybuilders, and some drug "experts," suffered premature deaths or serious health problems largely if not wholly because of their use of bodybuilding drugs. There'll be further high-profile premature deaths with strong suspicions of drug involvement, but for each of them there'll be many no-profile premature deaths related to drug use, and extensive health, relationship, family, financial, and crime-related problems about which the general public never hears.

REVELATION #5
Economics and Course #1

"If Course #1 is so effective, why isn't it popular today?" you may ask.

Because it's not in the interests of big business for this preeminent routine to be dominant. There's not much to sell related to it.

Properly informed bodybuilders know that, for outstanding progress in muscle growth, **Course #1** is the way to go, and all that's required is the following:

   a) *Basic training equipment*—free-weights alone will do the job.

   b) *Ordinary food*—food supplements aren't essential.

   c) *The guidance of Course #1*—no new training "secrets" are needed.

But there's not much business to be made out of that formula, and hardly any repeat business.

Bodybuilders can make terrific progress from a method that's been around for decades—a simple, low-cost method that doesn't require high-tech exercise equipment, gimmicks, food supplements, or new training instruction. That's not a welcome state of affairs for most companies that make money out of bodybuilders; so, for those companies, it's best that bodybuilding is made out to be complicated, mysterious, and costly.

Some exercise machines can be helpful, however, and some food supplements may be helpful, but neither are essential. Peary made his amazing progress long before the days of modern exercise equipment and food supplements.

REVELATION #6
Genetics

First illustration

A friend told me about when he started bodybuilding in the 1940s, well before anabolic steroids were around in the bodybuilding world. He had three training partners, in Leeds, England. Although all four young men were highly committed to their training, one of them made dramatically more progress than the others. Very soon that superman started winning physique contests. His name was Reg Park, and he became one of bodybuilding's first superstars—three-time Mr. Universe, and the first bodybuilder to bench press 500 pounds (227 kilos).

Reg inherited fantastic genetics for bodybuilding, and that, in combination with his dedication to bodybuilding, produced spectacular results.

Second illustration

At college in Liverpool, England, in the late 1970s, I trained at a gym where one of Europe's leading physiques worked out. We often trained at the same time.

This man was on steroids, and he had terrific genetics for bodybuilding other than for one body part. I had better calf development even though I was drug-free and had been training for far fewer years. He even asked me for advice on how he could improve his calves. But he hadn't neglected them. He knew they were his weakness.

The explanation for the difference in our calf development was solely in our heredity. I had better genetics for calf development, but he was much better off in all other body parts. I trained my calves similarly to how I trained my arms, chest and shoulders, but my calves were more responsive than those other muscle groups.

Never mind about the training routines that genetic supermen prosper on, especially when those men are bolstered with bodybuilding drugs.

Those routines are a total waste for most bodybuilders.

REVELATION #7
Hard gainers and easy gainers

Most bodybuilders find progress hard to make, hence the term "hard gainer." A hard gainer is the genetically average (or even disadvantaged), drug-free person, usually male, that typifies gym members. Hard gainers are usually naturally thin, although there are fat hard gainers. Hard gainers respond poorly, or not at all, to conventional training methods.

Conventional training advice creates permanent hard gainers, and shackles them in stagnation and frustration. Because the conventional advice works well for so few drug-free bodybuilders, it makes most bodybuilders believe that developing much bigger muscles is far more difficult than it really is.

There's a spectrum of "gainingness." At the "easiest" end are the super easy gainers (like Schwarzenegger, Park and all other physique stars) who have or had fantastically responsive physiques. These genetic freaks, and I'm not using "freaks" in a pejorative sense, are very rare—they constitute under 1% of the training population.

Bodybuilding's genetic phenomena have a blend of body structure, muscle insertion points, muscle belly length, muscle fiber type and number, neuromuscular efficiency, tendency for leanness, recuperative powers and resistance to injury that gives them tremendously responsive bodies, with potential for muscle development far in excess of that of the typical person. And for competitive bodybuilding there are important aesthetic factors that are also genetically determined.

Most bodybuilders get nowhere simply because they don't train well enough for long enough. But even had the youthful Woody Allen trained with greater dedication than the youthful Schwarzenegger, and taken even more steroids, Schwarzenegger's physique would still have outclassed Allen's by far, due to their genetic disparity for bodybuilding.

Behind the super easy gainers are the "regular" easy gainers who are able to gain to some degree on most programs, although they don't have the potential to become fantastic unless they are stoked up on bodybuilding drugs. There's a significant number of these regular easy gainers, perhaps as many as 10% or so of a random sample of typical bodybuilders. It's this group that provides gyms with most of their successes, but these bodybuilders usually use training routines that produce little or no progress for hard gainers. (And many trainers and coaches are also regular easy gainers; but some of them are, or were, super easy gainers.)

While regular easy gainers typically follow conventional methods, and make gains from them, they make far better progress when they adopt routines like **Course #1**.

Bodybuilders who play down the importance of genetics are almost always those who were dealt a better-than-average hand of genetics for bodybuilding. Few bodybuilders care to think that they got something relatively easily. They prefer to give the impression that they had to suffer for every smidgen they gained.

Of course, as easy gainers close in on their potential for muscle mass they can find gains hard to make. But until then, they found gains straightforward. They trained, and they grew. But real hard gainers find gains hard to make from day one unless they train as this book teaches.

Anyone blessed with a very responsive physique can never get in the shoes of a true hard gainer.

Once you recognize you're a hard gainer you set the stage for adopting effective training methods. Then you'll start to get good results. And eventually you may discover that what you thought was a modest potential for bodybuilding is actually a lot more.

Although "hard gainer" is a well used term in the bodybuilding world, it's a misnomer. Because hard gainers are the majority, it would be more accurate to call them "normal gainers." As it is, "hard gainer" implies a condition that's unusual.

The instruction in this book is primarily aimed at bodybuilders who can't make good progress from conventional methods—*hard gainers*—but by following the advice in this book you can realize terrific gains and, relatively speaking, make yourself into an easy gainer.

The composition of Peary Rader's gains and mine

By his own account, Peary gained almost 90 pounds (40 kilos) in about two years. We don't know the precise composition of that gain, but we do know that it transformed him from "a bag of bones" adult (128 pounds or 58 kilos, at 5-10 or 178 cms) into a heavyweight Olympic lifting champion, and that couldn't have occurred without a lot of additional muscle.

I gained 60 pounds (27 kilos), which I estimate was a 45-15 muscle-fat gain, but I can't be sure of the precise proportion. I didn't monitor my body composition. What I do know, however, is that gain transformed me from a very skinny adult into someone who deadlifted 400 pounds (182 kilos) for 20 reps—and that couldn't have happened without a lot of additional muscle.

Any fat gained along with muscle is easily lost if you go about it correctly. The additional muscle makes it easier to shed the fat. The greater muscle mass you have, the greater your caloric requirements. You can eat more than you could at a lower muscle mass, and yet still lose fat.

Expectations have been distorted today because of the stupendous gains that today's monster bodybuilders have amassed. Some of them have gained over 100 pounds (45 kilos) of muscle. But their progress can't be compared fairly with Peary's and mine. Neither Peary nor myself inherited freaky genetics for bodybuilding, and neither of us used bodybuilding drugs.

Genetic advantages and drug assistance make an enormous difference. Few people know the extent of the contribution of bodybuilding drugs to the physiques of the big-name bodybuilders since the 1960s. And only a few people know the specifics of the massive use of drugs by big-name bodybuilders. It's jaw-dropping!

But in the real world of drug-free bodybuilding for genetically typical trainees, Peary's progress, and mine, was outstanding, and the methods responsible are fully applicable to others.

REVELATION #8
Substance first, detail later

Build muscular substance before you concern yourself with muscular detail, but without adding excessive body fat.

If you try to build every aspect of your physique simultaneously, and maintain a high level of definition, you'll never build substantial overall muscle mass. That strategy just doesn't work well for drug-free, genetically typical bodybuilders, and that's one of the key reasons why you should never base your own training on the methods used by modern-day champion bodybuilders.

The strategy you require for building substantial muscle mass necessitates that you temporarily set aside perfect harmony of development and a high level of definition. You can't have it all while you actually build the substantial muscle mass, but you *can* work on the harmony and definition in between cycles of **Course #1**, so that everything falls into place over time.

Genetically gifted bodybuilders, and those on bodybuilding drugs, can build substance while they also work on detail, but not so other bodybuilders. Drug-assisted genetic phenomena may also be able to build substantial size in a limited area of their physiques without much if any growth elsewhere. But that's of no concern for drug-free, genetically typical bodybuilders.

If you want to add 3 inches (7.5 cms) of muscle to your arms, for example, you'll need to build around 30 to 40 pounds (14 to 18 kilos) of muscle over your whole physique. You can't do that by focusing on your arms.

About two thirds of your body's total muscle mass is in your thighs, buttocks and back. Your shoulders, chest, abs, arms, forearms and calves make up only about a third of your total muscle mass. **Course #1** focuses on your thigh-hip-back structure and, when properly applied, yields substantial growth in that large area. But the same routine also produces growth elsewhere.

To build yourself up substantially, focus on big exercises, not detail exercises. To draw an analogy, *don't use a toothpick when the job requires a pickax.*

Course #1 builds muscle mass—lots of it. But to do that, it employs pickax exercises, not toothpick exercises, to continue with the analogy.

Between cycles of Course #1—in order to ensure balanced strength and musculature throughout your physique—use sensible routines that include some good exercises that aren't on the list for Course #1. But don't add exercises to any of the Course #1 schedules.

REVELATION #9
The necessity of abbreviated training

Course #1 epitomizes *abbreviated training*. To stimulate muscle growth, you must train hard—with sufficient intensity. To give yourself the best chance of doing that, you must limit the quantity of training you do. The more training you do, the more exercise you have to spread your limited energy over.

Furthermore, to avoid overtraining and excessive demands on your recovery ability, you must limit the quantity of training you do. Then you'll be able to recuperate between workouts without undue delay.

So, for multiple reasons, abbreviated training is essential.

A fundamental principle behind abbreviated training is that just one of the best exercises works a lot of musculature *directly*, and another mass of muscle *indirectly*. Just a few of the best exercises work almost the entire physique. For example, there's not much muscle left untrained (directly or indirectly) from hard work on the barbell squat, the bench press, and the chin-up—and that's just one illustration of the three most fundamental training motions: a squat- or deadlift-type exercise, an upper-body press, and an upper-body pull.

When Peary made his amazing progress, he followed a routine with just four exercises in it. That's proof that the right abbreviated routine, properly applied, is hugely effective.

Peary Rader and his promotion of Course #1

Peary promoted versions of **Course #1** throughout his 50-year tenure of *Iron Man* magazine, although he didn't refer to the routine by that particular name. And he especially targeted the routine at hard gainers, a term he used himself. He wrote about the routine in many articles, and published many accounts of it written by others. And in an additional publication—*The Rader Master Bodybuilding and Weight Gaining System*—he gave special attention to the routine. This publication was first published in 1946, and a modernized version of it (48 pages) was published in 1956.

He even mentioned the routine (and a summary of what it did for him) in correspondence with me in the 1980s, about 50 years after he first used the course himself.

But Peary never wrote about the routine with the thoroughness that's provided in this book.

While he gave the greatest emphasis to the barbell squat as the primary exercise for **Course #1**, Peary noted that some people preferred the deadlift to the barbell squat, while some others preferred the hip-belt squat.

Different accounts of Peary's own amazing progress reported different durations of the routine. The one I reported on page 12 is what I consider to be the most precise, and it's from the 1956 version of *The Rader Master Bodybuilding and Weight Gaining System*. But some other reports referred to a shorter period, and rounded up the total gain. For example, in the March 1967 issue of *Iron Man*, Peary summarized his gain as "nearly 100 pounds in one year."

REVELATION #10
The magic of the barbell squat

The barbell squat is a super exercise *provided* you perform it safely for an adequate range of motion, and do so intensively and with an incrementally ever-greater poundage.

The more efficiently you squat, the greater the potential benefits. How efficiently you squat is mostly a result of the relative lengths of your torso, thighbones and shinbones.

One of the most important bodybuilding-related tasks you can set for yourself is to learn how to squat correctly—preferably to just below the position at which the top of your upper thighs is parallel to the floor, which is what some people refer to as the "full squat."

If you can do the full squat safely and intensively, *rejoice*—that's the ideal. But squatting to "just" the position at which the top of your upper thighs is parallel to the floor can still be very effective.

Depth of squatting is a function of hip position. The lower your hips, the deeper your squat. With just a broomstick over your upper back, heels about hip-width apart and each foot flared about 30 degrees, and your knees shoved out as you descend and ascend, squat while an assistant observes you from the side. With the help of your assistant's feedback, get the feel of the relative heights of your hips and knees at the bottom position as you vary the depth of the squat, and the resulting variation in the position of the top of your upper thighs.

Don't give up on the barbell squat because of initial difficulties. After you've become supple, and truly mastered squatting technique, you may be able to squat much more effectively than you can now. The technique instruction in this book will teach you how to squat.

But many bodybuilders legitimately can't barbell squat well—and particularly can't squat low enough safely. This is usually due to structural issues. A person with, proportionately speaking, long thighbones and shinbones but a short torso is always going to struggle in the squat, and perhaps to such a degree that he can never obtain substantial benefit from the exercise. Such bodybuilders need an alternative to the barbell squat. But leg extensions won't cut it. And although the leg press is much more effective than the leg extension, it's not good enough to substitute for the barbell squat in **Course #1**.

The barbell squat or the right alternative is so important that just that one exercise is the foundation of any workout of Course #1. It's the *linchpin* exercise. And unless you do the linchpin exercise as required, Course #1 won't work its magic no matter what you do with the rest of each workout.

REVELATION #11

The squat alternatives

The parallel-grip deadlift is the primary alternative to the barbell squat. It's tailor-made for bodybuilders who don't squat as efficiently as they deadlift. The parallel-grip deadlift works a similar mass of muscle as the barbell squat, but with reduced strain on the lower back (when it's done with correct technique).

While the barbell squat can be done in almost all gyms, the parallel-grip deadlift requires a special bar—a trap bar or, preferably, a shrug bar. Although these bars are readily available, most gyms don't have one. A parallel-grip bar should be a required piece of equipment for all gyms. It's far more valuable and much less costly than many pieces of equipment that most gym owners consider essential. Encourage the management of where you train to get a parallel-grip bar.

Because the parallel-grip deadlift is a recent innovation, few bodybuilders have experienced its tremendous benefits. It's the equal of the barbell squat for many bodybuilders, and for some it can be a more effective exercise.

When **Course #1** was first devised, parallel-grip deadlift bars weren't available, but they are now.

The barbell squat and the parallel-grip deadlift are so potentially potent that they are "growing exercises." Choose the one that's most suited to you. While some bodybuilders have comparable suitability for both, most are more suited to one than the other.

Another recommended alternative to the barbell squat is the hip-belt squat. This puts very little loading on the back, and keeps the stress primarily on the thighs and hips. It requires a special set-up but not a special bar. Of the three linchpin exercises, the hip-belt squat is the simplest to perform, and has the lowest risk. Provided all three are done properly, the barbell squat and the parallel-grip deadlift are more effective for building overall muscle mass because they involve more musculature than the hip-belt squat. *But if you really can't barbell squat or parallel-grip deadlift as required—especially if you have a back problem that precludes the aforementioned two exercises—use the hip-belt squat instead.*

In many cases, alternating the hip-belt squat with the barbell squat *or* the parallel-grip deadlift, from workout to workout, may be the best option. In other words, do the hip-belt-squat on Tuesday and the barbell squat on Saturday, for example; or, if you're more suited to the parallel-grip deadlift than the barbell squat, do the hip-belt squat on Tuesday and the parallel-grip deadlift on Saturday.

With three linchpin exercises to choose from—barbell squat, parallel-grip deadlift, and hip-belt squat—many more bodybuilders can benefit from Course #1 than could if using the barbell squat was the only way to go.

REVELATION #12
The advantages of the parallel-grip deadlift

Here are five big advantages of the parallel-grip deadlift over the barbell squat:

   a) The resistance is held beneath the body rather than precariously near the top of the spine, and thus there's no bar bearing down on you.

   b) Good form may be easier to maintain because the parallel-grip deadlift is technically less demanding than the barbell squat.

   c) Spotters aren't needed.

   d) No squat stands, power rack or safety bars are needed.

   e) The exercise is easily done from a dead stop at the bottom.

The same big advantages also apply to the hip-belt squat, although this exercise isn't normally done from a dead stop at the bottom.

So, generally speaking, the parallel-grip deadlift carries a lower level of risk than the barbell squat. But that's not to say the parallel-grip deadlift is inherently safe, and the barbell squat is inherently dangerous.

When comparing the same degree of descent of the hips, you may find that the parallel-grip deadlift works your thighs more than the barbell squat. It's not necessary, for example, to descend in the parallel-grip deadlift until the top of your upper thighs is parallel to the floor in order to mimic the effect on the thighs from barbell squatting to parallel. But some bodybuilders, because of their body structure, don't get much thigh development from the barbell squat, but can get substantial thigh development from the parallel-grip deadlift (even without a large degree of knee flexion).

The parallel-grip deadlift also has big advantages over the straight-bar, bent-legged deadlift. The parallel-grip deadlift reduces spine stress, puts the hands and arms into more efficient positions, yields more knee flexion, and simplifies technique. And when comparing sets of similar intensity using correct technique, the parallel-grip deadlift probably produces less systemic fatigue than the straight-bar deadlift, and thus probably requires less recovery time between workouts. *For these reasons, it's the parallel-grip deadlift that's employed in* **Course #1** *as a linchpin exercise, not the conventional deadlift.*

Initially, the parallel-grip deadlift was called the *trap-bar deadlift* because the trap bar was the device most often used for it. The rhombus-shaped trap bar was developed by Al Gerard in a successful effort to enable him to deadlift without the back problems he experienced from the straight-bar deadlift. Over recent years, the shrug bar has provided a variation that permits more leg room because of its hexagonal shape. And there are other ways of performing the parallel-grip deadlift—rectangular and square bars, some specially bent bars that don't enclose the user, and even a Hammer Strength® machine.

Dumbbells can mimic a parallel-grip bar when they are held at the sides of the thighs using a parallel grip, but large dumbbells are unwieldy to use, and even small 'bells can get in the way of the legs and thighs. Dumbbells may also limit stance width and flare more than one-piece bars do, and thus hamper technique. Furthermore, because of the smaller circumference of their plates relative to the full-size barbell plates used on a parallel-grip bar, dumbbells lead to an excessive range of motion unless it's limited—perhaps by boxes or platforms.

REVELATION #13
The magic of 20 reps

The benefits from the barbell squat, the parallel-grip deadlift and the hip-belt squat don't come just from the localized muscular work. Provided these exercises are trained hard for high reps, with accompanying heavy, forced breathing, and incrementally heavier poundages over time, there's an anabolic effect that boosts overall muscle growth. There may even be a testosterone upsurge from each bout of it.

If 21 or 18 reps had been chosen and initially championed, for example, the bodybuilding results would have been the same, but 20 was chosen and quickly established as the "magic" number.

The 20-rep style means performing one rep at a time, with heavy, forced breathing between reps. The brief breather between reps is called the *rest pause*.

Intensive 20-rep barbell squatting and parallel-grip deadlifting have to be experienced before they can be fully appreciated. Just a single set is a workout in itself—a test of body and spirit. Intensive 20-rep hip-belt squatting is also very demanding, but not as grueling as the other two.

The 20-rep work is the *linchpin* of **Course #1**. But you must take your time to adapt gradually to the demands involved. Don't jump in at the deep end. The demands aren't just muscular. Your heart and lungs need to adapt, as does your entire support structure including your shoulder girdle, vertebral column, and feet.

Performing each workout's linchpin exercise *AS SPECIFIED*—with correct technique, sufficient effort, and enough poundage progression—is *MANDATORY*. Without it, Course #1 doesn't exist.

Even if you perform the rest of the training schedule as required, and do everything outside of the gym as required, you'll still have *NEXT TO NOTHING if you don't do each workout's linchpin exercise AS SPECIFIED*.

But once you do perform each workout's linchpin exercise with correct technique and sufficient effort, it's *MANDATORY* that you perform the rest of the training schedule as required, *AND* do everything outside the gym as required. Then you'll be able to respond to the growth stimulation from the 20-rep work, and thus be able to gradually build up the poundage of each workout's linchpin exercise, and eventually make it very impressive, *AS IS REQUIRED*.

Depending on which workout schedule(s) you use, you may employ just one linchpin exercise per cycle of **Course #1**, or perhaps two of them.

REVELATION #14
The quantity of muscle you can build

The most spectacular muscle growth is made by men who used to have super physiques who rebuild their former development while assisted by anabolic steroids. Keep that in mind when some supermen boast about their spectacular progress.

How much muscle you'll build on **Course #1** depends on many factors including your age, gender, genetics, motivation, and how close you are to your bodybuilding potential. It's also hugely affected by how well you train, how well you satisfy the components of recuperation, and how long and often you follow **Course #1**.

If you've made little or no bodybuilding progress so far, you'll have more potential for building muscle than someone who has already built a lot.

If you're male, you'll have more potential than if you're female.

If you're 25, you'll probably have more potential than if you're 55.

If you're a strong, athletic, well-built, barrel-chested man even without any training, and you have long muscle bellies and a thick bone structure, you'll have far more potential for bodybuilding than if you're non-athletic, skinny and lanky.

No matter what your potential is for building muscle, if you apply yourself only half-heartedly to the training part of **Course #1**, and cut corners with your recuperation, you'll make no progress.

But if you fully commit to **Course #1**, including at least four months of *The Growth Phase*, and fully satisfy all the requirements in and out of the gym, you *will* make good progress. How much will vary for the reasons already noted, but around 10 to 15 pounds (4.5 to 7.0 kilos), with most of it being muscle, is realistic for most male bodybuilders. And for drug-free, genetically typical bodybuilders, that's terrific progress.

The Growth Phase **is the period during which you train hard, fully satisfy the components of recuperation (including consuming a surplus of calories and nutrients), handle ever-greater personal best exercise weights, and go well into new exercise poundage territory.**

Apply Course #1 properly for a full cycle once every 12 months or so, for a few years, and you'll be transformed— it can add up to 50 pounds (23 kilos) of muscle in some cases. It's not possible to respond like this indefinitely, but several successful cycles spread over a few consecutive years is realistic provided you're sufficiently dedicated.

But claims of building 20 to 30 pounds (9 to 14 kilos) of *muscle*, drug-free, in just six to eight weeks, are fanciful. Such a rate of progress isn't realistic for drug-free, typical bodybuilders.

Course #1 is a method of *bulking* because it builds a lot of mass, but the mass must be mostly muscle. Packing on just fat isn't bodybuilding.

To try to maximize your recovery ability during *The Growth Phase*, you must consume a sufficient surplus of calories and protein from healthy food. To try to be sure of this, accept a small but temporary increase in your body fat level. If you try to keep your gains pure muscle, you'll probably not consume enough food, and thus hinder if not prohibit muscle growth. It's best to oversupply nourishment rather than risk undersupplying it. But the oversupply doesn't mean gluttony and a heavy gain of body fat.

Some bodybuilders who misinterpreted the nutritional component of **Course #1** consumed such an excess of food (including milk) that they gained far more fat than muscle. This is where the gains of 20 or more pounds in six to eight weeks come from. But when those gains are mostly fat, the results are disappointing because they aren't physique enhancing.

A *three-quarters/one-quarter* muscle/fat gain, or perhaps *two-thirds/one-third*, is the proportion to aim for. Then, between cycles of **Course #1**, trim the excess body fat. This is the traditional bulking-trimming strategy that's been around since long before steroids.

The idea, for example, is to "bulk up" 15 pounds (7 kilos) over a few months, with just a quarter to a third of it being body fat, then *slowly* shed that fat in a trimming cycle to yield a net gain of about 10 to 12 pounds (4.5 to 5.5 kilos) of muscle.

But bulking up 10 pounds of fat and then trimming off 10 pounds of fat is a waste of time and food. Some super bulkers have packed on 50 or more pounds over just a few months, almost all of it fat, but then after they had shed the fat they ended up with a net gain of no more than just a few pounds of muscle. In some cases there was a net *loss* of muscle because so little muscle was built during the bulking stage, and then during the trimming stage the fat loss wasn't done correctly and muscle was lost along with the fat.

"Trimming" doesn't mean getting "ripped" at well under 10% body fat. Leave the super definition until you've built all the muscle you want for the time being. Drug-free, genetically typical bodybuilders can't build muscle while they are "ripped."

Peary Rader's alternatives to the standard barbell squat

Peary was probably the most influential advocate of high-rep squats and abbreviated training, but even he acknowledged that some people are better suited to the standard barbell squat than others. He promoted the use of a cambered (curved) bar for squatting—not just to remove some of the discomfort of the exercise for those who don't have favorable leverages for the squat, but to give a further boost for those who do have favorable leverages. Joseph Curtis Hise invented the cambered bar for the squat.

Peary promoted and also sold the "magic circle" (invented by James E. Douglass)—a metal ring attached to a harness. The harness is suspended on the shoulders, with the ring at about hip height, and weight plates loaded on the ring. It yields benefits, especially for those not well suited to the barbell squat. I used to have one. But technique difficulties still remain for those who aren't well suited to the barbell squat. (Furthermore, you're unlikely to ever come across a magic circle today—it's a custom-made piece of equipment that's not readily available.)

The best way to eliminate technique difficulties of the barbell squat, the cambered bar squat, and the magic circle squat, is to substitute the parallel-grip deadlift or the hip-belt squat.

REVELATION #15
The *enhanced* version in contrast with the *traditional* version

Course #1 promoted in this book is the *enhanced* version. The ways in which it differs from the *traditional* one are explained in this book, but here's a summary of the main differences:

Enhanced	Incorporates the thorough, structured *Foundation Phase*.
Traditional	Doesn't incorporate a thorough, structured foundation phase.
Enhanced	Provides a choice of three linchpin exercises according to individual suitability—barbell squat, parallel-grip deadlift, and hip-belt squat.
Traditional	Usually prescribes just one linchpin exercise—barbell squat.
Enhanced	Provides substantial allowance for variation in exercise selection.
Traditional	Provides less allowance for variation in exercise selection.
Enhanced	May include specific training to strengthen the grip.
Traditional	Doesn't include specific training to strengthen the grip.
Enhanced	Comprises 20 reps per set of a linchpin exercise and the breathing pullover or the Rader chest pull, and around 10 reps for midsection work. But for the other exercises there are several set-rep format options.
Traditional	Comprises 20 reps per set for the barbell squat and the breathing pullover or the Rader chest pull, about the same count for calf and ab work, and around 10 to 12 reps for the remaining exercises.
Enhanced	While hard work is essential on the 20-rep work, extreme intensity isn't required.
Traditional	Commonly urges excessive intensity for the 20-rep work.
Enhanced	Typically employs two groups of exercises, alternated from workout to workout.
Traditional	Typically employs the same group of exercises at each workout.
Enhanced	Requires great care to be given to applying correct exercise technique.
Traditional	Typically, insufficient care is given to applying correct exercise technique.

Enhanced	Employs a maximum of two workouts per week, and allows for flexibility with training frequency according to individual recuperative powers.
Traditional	Typically prescribes two or three workouts each week.
Enhanced	Gives specific guidance on the right degree of nutritional surplus.
Traditional	Tends to encourage excessive nutritional surplus.
Enhanced	Employs a longer duration of each cycle but a slower, safer and more practical rate of exercise poundage increase and bodyweight gain.
Traditional	Employs a shorter duration of each cycle and attempts to hasten the rate of exercise poundage increase and bodyweight gain.
Enhanced	Typically results in a greater proportion of bodyweight gain as muscle.
Traditional	Typically results in a lesser proportion of bodyweight gain as muscle.

COMPULSORY understanding, for bodybuilding success

This book is about how to apply **Course #1**. This routine *requires* hard training and incrementally ever-greater exercise poundages—they are essential elements. (Some other good routines for drug-free, genetically typical bodybuilders don't require such a degree of hard training, or as much focus on ever-greater exercise poundages.)

But excessive training intensity and/or incorrect application of ever-greater exercise poundages will put you at risk of serious injury, and undermine your mental resilience and passion for training.

And even if your training is correct, if you overdo your rate of bodyweight gain, you'll hinder your efforts to improve your physique.

I've painstakingly described the correct application of training intensity, exercise poundage increments, and bodyweight gain, so that you can apply **Course #1** properly, for the best results.

REVELATION #16
Individual variation

Other than identical siblings, no two people are the same genetically. But even though genetically identical brothers could train together on the same routine, they would still vary in important factors that affect bodybuilding progress—training enthusiasm and dedication, nutrition, sleeping habits and rest in general, work, family commitments, and so on.

Everyone else varies in almost all considerations, including genetic potential for muscle growth, the training equipment that's available, suitability or otherwise of some exercises, training enthusiasm and the ability to tolerate exercise-induced discomfort, age, health, nutrition, sleeping habits and rest in general, and work and family commitments. Each of these considerations alone can undermine bodybuilding progress.

This explains why different people respond differently to the same training regimen. Individualization of Course #1 is required. How to do this will be explained.

Peary Rader's suitability for the barbell squat

Peary noted that he "squatted almost vertically." Although there must be some forward lean while barbell squatting, his comment indicates that he had very good leverages for the squat. (People not well suited to the squat lean forward in an exaggerated way, and usually can't squat deeply without rounding their lower backs.) Peary found it straightforward to squat with ideal technique (including a good depth of motion), and was able to squat hard with minimal risk of injury. And that, in combination with the great dedication he applied to Course #1, produced amazing results. The squat was his ultimate "growing exercise." But at that time, the squat wasn't a popular exercise—and some influential people in the Iron Game forcefully opposed it. Peary was part of a pioneering movement.

At the time, the only interpretation of Course #1 was the one with the barbell squat as the linchpin exercise. Had Peary not been structurally well suited to the squat, it's unlikely that he would have come across an alternative exercise that would have been so effective. As a result, he almost certainly would never have experienced the amazing results he did. Then he wouldn't have had the great success story to publicize, *Iron Man* magazine wouldn't have existed, and Peary would never have been a force in the Iron Game.

REVELATION #17

Desire, determination and dedication

Achieving your bodybuilding potential demands extraordinary desire, determination and dedication applied to the proper instruction.

There's no place for half measures, laziness, lukewarm enthusiasm, or the wrong instruction.

If you don't train properly, rest properly, sleep properly and eat properly—*consistently*—you'll get nowhere or make only minimal progress. You've got to pay your dues.

The components of successful bodybuilding are simple once you really know what you're doing, but putting them into practice requires 100% commitment.

But these aren't my rules. I'm just the messenger.

When done properly, bodybuilding is a fantastic activity. Don't miss your chance to benefit from it.

Apply Course #1.

2

Remember this Chinese proverb: *"The man who removes a mountain begins by carrying away small stones."*

Bodybuilding exemplifies this incremental process. Get each rep right, each set right, each workout right, each day's nutrition right, each day's rest right, and each night's sleep right, and then do that again and again and again . . . .

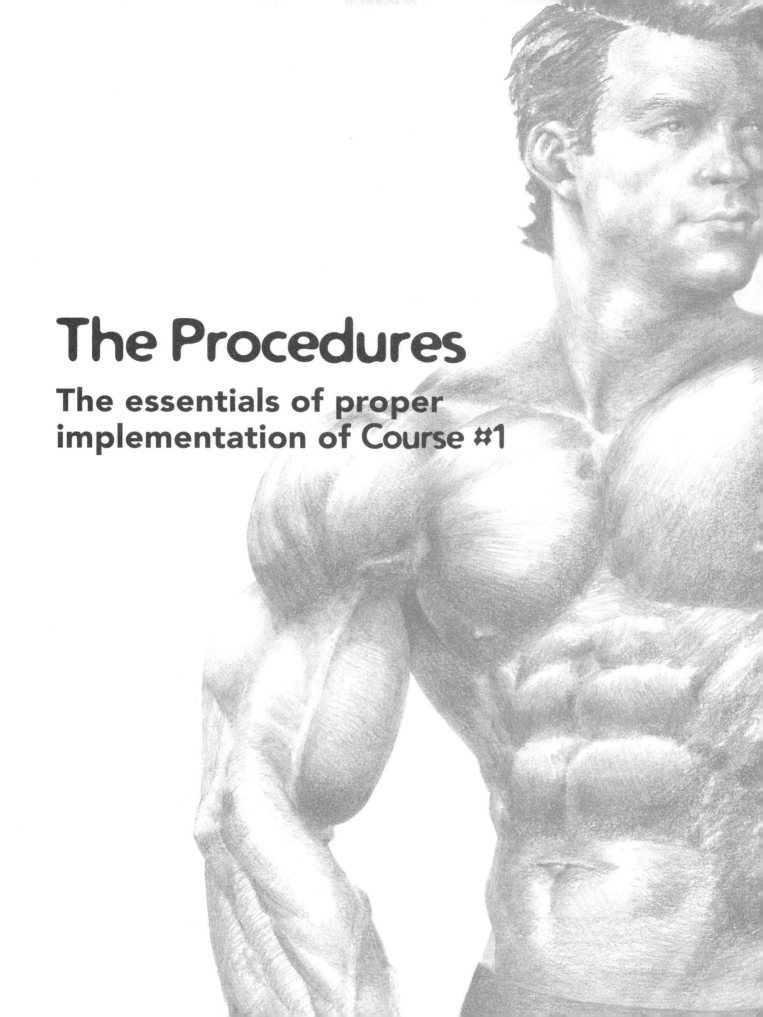

The Procedures

The essentials of proper implementation of Course #1

PROCEDURE #1
Fully attend to the components of recuperation

This *Procedure* is presented first to underline its importance.

Without fully satisfying all the components of recuperation you'll make little or no progress on Course #1 no matter how hard you may train or how well you may satisfy most of the other aspects of training.

What you do in the gym provides the stimulus for muscle growth, but to be able to respond to the stimulus you must stay out of the gym long enough to permit your body to repair the muscle damage *and* build a little extra tissue. (The "little extra tissue" is the *overcompensation*.) Then return to the gym for another bout of growth stimulation. If you train too often, you won't give your body enough time to repair the broken-down muscle tissue *and* build the overcompensation tissue. The overcompensation accumulates over weeks and months to produce bigger muscles.

But recovery time between workouts, including sufficient sleep, is only part of the anabolic environment. You must also provide food in sufficient quantity and quality—that's where the raw materials for muscle growth come from.

The better you satisfy the elements of recovery, the better you'll recuperate from your training, and the more likely that you'll be able to make progress at your next workout.

PROCEDURE #2
Be sure where you train is conducive to progress

Although most people may think of gyms as specialist places such as a Gold's Gym, gyms can also be found at health clubs, YMCAs, colleges, universities, leisure centers, and some schools. You have no control over the equipment unless you can influence the management, but you do have control over what equipment you use, and how you use it.

Equipment other than the basics usually diverts attention from where it should be focused. Put pec deck, cable crossover and leg extension machines in a gym, for example, and most members will probably use that equipment. Then not only do members usually lose sight of training priorities, but so do gym owners and instructors.

The presence of inferior equipment *and* well-maintained basic training gear gives you a choice. But if there's no squat rack or power rack, for example, and the free-weights equipment in general is poor, you need to look elsewhere.

How to make a gym work

a) Train when the gym isn't busy.

b) Take your own little discs and lifters' chalk if the gym doesn't have them.

c) Keep your mind on your training and stay clear of distractions.

d) Learn from this book how to train, and then take charge of your training. Don't surrender that authority to others.

e) Never use any exercise equipment just because it's available. Use only what's best for you.

f) Try to persuade the gym's management to buy a parallel-grip deadlift bar (trap bar or, preferably, a shrug bar), a cambered squat bar, and a power rack, if it doesn't already have them. The bars are inexpensive relative to machines, and will add greatly to the gym's functional value for all members. If the management isn't interested, offer to buy one of the bars in return for a discount on membership. Win the management over on one bar, and perhaps it will get your other recommendations.

If you're interested in setting up your own home gym, see the detailed guidance included in a chapter of BEYOND BRAWN.

PROCEDURE #3
Use good machinery or no machinery at all

With a barbell and dumbbell set you can do the same exercises anywhere. Free-weights are almost universal in gyms, but good machinery isn't. The technique instruction for exercises that use free-weights is the same for all brands of that gear, but not so for machinery where, for example, the instructions for one brand's bench press machine may be different from another's. As a result of these factors, and others, free-weights are given priority in this book.

If, however, you have access to the generally good machinery—for example, Body Masters®, Cybex ®, Hammer Strength ®, MedX ®, and Nautilus ®—you could substitute it for the comparable free-weights exercises (other than the linchpin exercises, which should be done with free-weights for best results); but tread carefully. Some of the generally good machines can still cause irritations and injuries for some bodybuilders even when those machines are used correctly. And most machines can't accommodate all body sizes. Of course, free-weights exercises also cause problems if they aren't performed correctly.

A machine exercise may cause irritation, but the comparable free-weights exercise may not, and vice versa, depending on the individual, the exercise, and the particular piece of machinery.

Features of good machinery include smoothness of motion, ease of entry and exit, and the ability to accommodate a variety of body types through adjustment of seats, back pads, and movement arms.

Whenever you use a machine, follow the manufacturer's guidelines—very brief instructions are often fixed to the machines themselves. The correct set-up position is essential. For instance, on a shoulder machine, you may need to line up your shoulder joints with the pivot points.

Fine-tune your set-up until you find what feels most comfortable. You may need several workouts. A set-up that initially felt awkward may, after some adjustment, feel fine. Never push hard on a machine until after you've found a set-up that's proven safe for several workouts without producing any negative reaction.

Although high-tech machinery can be useful, it's not essential. Free-weights alone, properly used, have proven to be tremendously effective, and I commend them to you.

Course #1 has traditionally been performed exclusively with free-weights. In particular, the linchpin exercises should be done with free-weights for the best results.

PROCEDURE #4

Choose exercises that are well suited *to you*

Unless you choose exercises that are well suited *to you*, Course #1 won't work for you.

Don't choose exercises based on what appears to be most popular where you train, or in the bodybuilding publications you read. Exercises that may be suited to some other bodybuilders may not be suited to you.

Perhaps your most important exercise selection decision is between the barbell squat and the parallel grip deadlift. Few bodybuilders are equally suited to both, so it's imperative that you choose the one that's best for you.

How do you know which one is best for you? If you can barbell squat without leaning over excessively, and while keeping a slightly hollow lower spine even when the top of your upper thighs is just below parallel to the floor, you're definitely highly suited to the squat. But if you're an ungainly barbell squatter who leans forward a great deal, and your lower back rounds readily, try the parallel-grip deadlift instead.

But perhaps neither the barbell squat nor the parallel-grip deadlift are suited to you, and you need to resort to the hip-belt squat instead. For example, perhaps you have a back problem that precludes the barbell squat and the parallel-grip deadlift.

Easy gainers often have a physical structure that's suited to the barbell squat—one with short limbs relative to torso length. But hard gainers often have a physical structure suited to the deadlift—limbs that are long relative to torso length—and that's why many of them find the parallel-grip deadlift more effective than the barbell squat.

Many bodybuilders aren't well suited to the bench press. Sometimes, the same bodybuilders who find the parallel-grip deadlift better suited to them than the barbell squat, find the parallel bar dip to be better suited to them than the bench press. (A barrel-chested structure, with short arms and forearms, is highly suited to bench pressing.)

And here are two further illustrations of good exercise selection: Light people are usually more suited to the chin-up and the pull-up than heavy people. And while a heavy person will probably struggle with the conventional parallel bar dip, a dip machine will remove bodyweight as a factor.

To determine your depth of squatting accurately, and your back positioning at the bottom of the exercise, get an assistant to watch you from the side (while crouched, to view you from about your knee height), and provide you with instant feedback. You can't see what's happening in those areas from the reflection in a mirror in front of you, and you shouldn't watch yourself in a side-on mirror while you exercise.

PROCEDURE #5
Use correct exercise technique

Building bigger muscles hinges on the bedrock of correct exercise technique.

Hundreds of thousands of people, if not millions, have been forced to give up resistance training because of injuries caused by using incorrect exercise technique.

Correct technique is essential no matter which training routine you use, or what exercise intensity you apply. But the harder you train, the greater the importance of correct exercise technique.

Never apply the foolish "no pain, no gain" maxim.

Correct exercise technique (or form), is an essential component of **Course #1**.

When I was a youngster I had little or no time for anyone who talked or wrote about the possible dangers of training. Being so young I could, at first, get away with foolish training methods without much immediate discomfort. I persisted with harmful practices that included squatting with my heels raised on a board and the barbell too high on my shoulders, old-fashioned hack machine squatting, Smith machine squatting, bench pressing with a wide grip way too close to my neck, round-back deadlifting, explosive lifting, and specific cheating movements.

A few years later I was plagued with injuries, especially to my knees and back. Countless bodybuilders have experienced similar problems. I sustained most of those injuries because I used incorrect exercise technique. Much later I had the injuries fixed by non-invasive treatment, but in the meantime my training was devastated.

Exercise technique isn't simple. It requires detailed instruction and serious study if you're to master it.

Exercise technique is concerned with equipment set-up, grip, stance, body positioning, and bar pathways. But for safe training, correct exercise technique must be combined with a smooth, controlled rep speed.

Exercise technique and rep speed are separate issues, but integral parts of safe training.

PROCEDURE #6
Develop suppleness

Unless you're supple you'll be incapable of performing some key exercises correctly. For example, if your hamstrings (rear of your thighs) are tight, that will prohibit correct squatting and parallel-grip deadlifting because it will lead to premature rounding of your lower back.

A flexible body is also required for youthfulness, regardless of age.

Most people lack sufficient flexibility because of inactivity, or limited activity. Bodyweight and leverages also affect flexibility. A fat person, for example, may be inflexible largely because of the excess fat getting in the way.

While bodybuilding exercises can help to improve flexibility where suppleness may be lacking, specific stretching is needed, too.

Stretching elongates muscles, not tendons or ligaments. Tendons and ligaments are almost inelastic. Muscles need to be lengthened only a little to produce significant improvement in a joint's range of motion.

You need symmetrical suppleness. If you don't get both sides equally pliable you may promote asymmetrical exercise technique, which would increase the risk of injury. For example, assume that your right hamstrings are tighter than those on your left. When you squat to a sufficient depth, the less flexible right hamstrings would stop lengthening while the left ones keep lengthening. That would lead to asymmetrical exercise technique.

After a few months of regular performance of the prescribed stretches you may increase your flexibility substantially. Thereafter, keep stretching in order to maintain your improved flexibility.

PROCEDURE #7
Take action to remove physical hindrances

If you have difficulty with any of the stretches, and don't progress in flexibility as required, you may have scar tissue, adhesions, or other restrictions in your muscles. These hindrances commonly cause muscle, tendon and joint discomfort and pain. The hindrances need to be treated so that your muscles can return to their normal, supple, discomfort-free operation.

These hindrances can make correct performance of the major exercises an impossibility.

Many people mistakenly accept physical discomfort and restrictions. But with the right treatment you may be able to rid yourself of problems you may have accepted as permanent, or at least reduce them greatly. To address the problems, you need the help of more than chiropractic, osteopathy, physical therapy, and orthodox medicine. Those professions don't address soft-tissue problems like some other therapies do.

Illustrations of the benefits from soft-tissue therapy

Soft-tissue or myofascial restrictions had hampered my training for many years. For example, those restrictions had impaired my quadriceps, which in turn caused knee problems and pain. Over that period I was never able to progress with stretching my quadriceps despite consistent efforts. Then in August 2003, non-invasive, myofascial therapy by Dr. James Kiernan—Active Release Techniques® (ART®)—removed the restrictions in my thighs, including adhesions between my right vastus lateralis and iliotibial band. The flexibility in my quadriceps increased instantly, and increased further over the following weeks. It was only after the restrictions had been released that the quadriceps stretching became effective. Furthermore, my kneecaps tracked correctly, and my knees were free of discomfort. My knees were transformed.

For many years I was unable to perform lateral flexion of my neck or lower back without discomfort. I had impaired lateral flexion throughout my spine, which led to numerous injuries. ART® transformed my neck and lower back.

I regained ranges of motion throughout my body I'd not had for many years. I could perform yoga postures I'd been unable to since I was a teenager. I could perform resistance exercises safely that I'd been unable to for several years. The benefits from the myofascial therapy were dramatic.

Visit www.activerelease.com for a listing of certified ART providers. But there are many ART providers who aren't listed at that website, so ask around among therapists in general in your area.

Furthermore, visit a chiropractor—preferably one who is also trained in ART®—to see if you have one or more of common anomalies such as scoliosis, tilted pelvis, limbs that may appear to be different in length, excessive lordosis or other postural problems, spondylosis, foot problems, and flexion imbalances between one side of your body and the other. You may not be aware that you have any of these conditions, so it's important that you investigate the possibility.

Physical anomalies are common, and can influence whether or not certain exercises or specific variations of them are suited to you. What may be safe for most bodybuilders may be unsafe for you. And physical restrictions that don't receive appropriate treatment commonly lead to training limitations, which in turn usually lead to increased restrictions and limitations.

PROCEDURE #8
Use a controlled rep speed

Lift the weight, don't throw it; and lower it, don't drop it. Never use fast or jerky movements. (Explosive movements, such as Olympic lifting, aren't included in **Course #1**.) Most bodybuilders perform their reps too quickly—they take only about one second for each phase of a rep, or even less time in some cases.

Let rep *smoothness* be your guide. If your reps are smooth—including during the transition or turnaround between the positive and negative phases of a rep—you're using the required control.

In practice, smooth reps typically take no faster than two to three seconds for the positive phase, and no faster than another two to three seconds for the negative phase. For the positive phase of the final rep of a tough set, when you almost grind to a halt, you may need more than five seconds.

Some exercises have longer strokes than others, and thus need a longer duration to show comparable control. For example, the pulldown has a greater range of motion than the bench press, and the bench press has a greater range of motion than the shrug.

It's not necessary to perform reps extremely slowly. Outlandish claims are sometimes made on behalf of extremely slow training. Extremely slow reps aren't even a sure way to train safely. One of the most persistent injuries I've ever had was sustained while performing extremely slow reps. But I've sustained many injuries while performing reps quickly. Avoid fast reps, but there's no need to move to the other extreme.

The first few reps of a work set don't require the degree of effort that the final few do. As you fatigue, you need to increase your effort level. If you apply your full effort at the start of a set, the weight will move explosively and without the smooth control required for safe training. But toward the end of a hard set you'll need to apply your full effort in order to complete the reps.

But smooth, controlled reps can be performed with correct *or* incorrect exercise technique. Even if a smooth, controlled rep speed is used, if it's combined with incorrect exercise technique it will yield high-risk training.

Keep your reps smooth as you pay homage to correct exercise technique, effort, and poundage progression. Make each set perfect by making each rep perfect.

PROCEDURE #9

Train hard!

Once you're in *The Growth Phase* of **Course #1** you'll find out whether or not you really want bigger muscles. To stimulate muscle growth you must train *hard*—with sufficient intensity.

Very few bodybuilders train too hard. Most don't train hard enough.

No routine, gym, equipment, diet, supplement, writer, personality, course, book, seminar, or dvd exists to get you to drive yourself hard in the gym on a regular basis. The buck stops with you.

Deliver training ferocity!

To give yourself the best chance of training intensively you must limit the amount of training you do. This is why **Course #1** epitomizes *abbreviated training*.

Some bodybuilders find visualizations helpful. Try some, and see if they help you.

  a) With the bar loaded for a work set, switch to training mode. Switch off from your life. Become your training. Nothing else matters now.

  b) Perform one rep at a time. Look no further than the current rep. Don't rush. *Use correct exercise technique.*

  c) When the discomfort intensifies, dissociate yourself from it. Imagine you're watching yourself on film. Push on. *Use correct exercise technique.*

  d) Remind yourself of how much you want a better physique. Keep the reps coming. Don't rush. Push on. *Use correct exercise technique.*

  e) To be able to train hard is a privilege. Don't quit prematurely. Forge on. *Use correct exercise technique.*

  f) As the set nears completion, and you're at your hilt, perhaps imagine a vivid life-or-death situation where, if you fail to make a rep, you'll die. Then squeeze out another rep or two, *in correct exercise technique.*

Provided you follow **Course #1** properly, you'll learn to train harder and tolerate a greater degree of exercise-induced discomfort.

Imagine having an increased capacity for training *hard*. Imagine performing one, two, three or even more reps beyond what you do now in a given work set even though you may believe that you already train hard. One rep at a time, you'll keep *going* and *going* before you finally quit. When onlookers think you're spent, you'll surprise them and grind out yet another rep.

Once you're in *The Growth Phase*, make all your work sets heroic efforts. But those efforts must be supported by adequate recuperation so that you can sustain the proper rate of poundage progression for long enough to produce growth. *Progress is the bottom line, not training intensity per se.*

PROCEDURE #10

Use exercise intensifiers sparingly, if at all

Exercise intensifiers are supposed to take a set beyond the point at which you've completed the maximum number of reps under your own efforts with a constant weight. The intensifiers include drop sets, forced or assisted reps, negative-only reps, and partial or zone reps.

Intensifiers have no place in a beginner's schedule. Other bodybuilders may find them helpful when they are used sparingly. Intensifiers are commonly misused, with negative consequences. Here are the two major problems:

a) When you know, for instance, you have forced reps to do at the end of a planned eight-rep set of bench presses, you may intentionally or unintentionally conserve some energy for the forced reps. Rather than grind out the eighth rep, you stop after the seventh and then do the forced reps. And "forced" reps are often not done with full effort, with the result that the set would be extended but not intensified. It would be better, in this illustration, to get all eight reps and end it there, rather than cut the main set short in order to tack on some less-than-100%-effort "forced" reps.

b) For bodybuilders who really have the zeal to perform a full set of regular reps *and* give their all to an intensifier, they risk overtraining through training too hard. Provided you're already training with sufficient intensity, the use of an intensifier may hinder your progress.

During my youth I was fanatically motivated. During some periods I performed a set until I could no longer complete a rep, then an assistant helped me to perform several forced reps, and then with further assistance I finished with a few negative-only reps. The involved muscles were temporarily paralyzed. But I made no progress from that approach. Other bodybuilders have had the same experience.

But just one or two forced reps, *or* just one negative rep performed as slowly as possible, can be done to finish off just the final set of some exercises no more often than once a week *provided* that the main part of the set was performed correctly in each case. That sparing use of an intensifier may provide a jolt of growth stimulus that helps to sustain progress.

For safety reasons, forced reps or other intensifiers shouldn't be applied to these exercises from the **Course #1** schedules: barbell squat, parallel-grip deadlift, partial deadlift, and side bend. Furthermore, the breathing pullover and the Rader chest pull aren't suited to intensifiers.

PROCEDURE #11
Vary your training intensity over time

Although hard training is essential for building muscle and strength, it shouldn't be done at every workout of every week throughout the year. It must be interspersed between periods of less stressful training. This is particularly so for drug-free, genetically typical bodybuilders.

The correct application of effort is the essence of intensity variation. It's at the root of long-term, successful bodybuilding. Cutting back a little at the start of a new routine, or at the start of a new cycle of a familiar routine, and gradually building the poundages back, creates the momentum required to be able to go into new exercise poundage territory most readily.

"New exercise poundage territory" means an ever-greater personal best weight (in correct technique) for a given exercise for the particular rep count or range concerned. For an exercise that's new for you, you won't have a personal best weight for it, but you will the second cycle you use that exercise. For the first cycle you use that exercise, do the best you can even though you don't have a personal best poundage to better.

Beginners shouldn't be concerned with intensity variation. Provided training is appropriate, and recuperation is adequate, a beginner should be able to maintain steady progress for a year or more. Thereafter, however, some form of intensity variation is recommended.

It's not just your body that will rebel against consistent full-bore effort. Your mind will, too. There must be slack periods. There must be workouts where you purposely avoid pushing yourself to the limit. But intensity variation must be properly structured or otherwise it will be counterproductive.

Intensity variation is built into **Course #1**. During its *Growth Phase* it's possible to train hard every workout for several consecutive months, and make steady progress during that period, albeit a slow pace of growth. But a slow pace adds up over several months, and then really adds up when you perform several such cycles.

Many bodybuilders are fascinated with set-rep schemes, training volume, exercise selection, nutritional ins and outs, supplement fads, and other issues. Their knowledge may be almost encyclopedic.

But when they actually work out, they never really train hard.

The most important aspect of effective training is the most difficult to satisfy—*hard work*.

PROCEDURE #12
Build strength

The biggest physiques aren't the strongest, and the strongest aren't the biggest, but how many well-developed men do you know who aren't way stronger than undeveloped men? And how many very strong bodybuilders do you know who don't also have well-developed muscles?

Additional to training differences, other factors (all genetically determined) help to account for the variations in muscle size among individuals of similar strength levels, including leverages, muscle composition factors, and neurological efficiency. Some strength specialists (not bodybuilders) are super strong yet don't have large muscles—including elite powerlifters and Olympic weightlifters who compete at the lower bodyweights.

But generally speaking, when you can handle much larger poundages *in correct exercise form*—especially for medium or higher reps—you'll have built bigger muscles. This particularly applies to bodybuilding beginners and intermediates, who are the farthest from realizing their potential for muscle mass.

Correctly applying incrementally ever-greater resistance is at the heart of **Course #1**.

But it's not the weight added to an exercise that possibly causes muscle growth. The ability to handle additional weight on a given exercise comes about only *after* the body has adapted to stimulation from previous workouts, which may include a tiny increase in muscle mass.

Your body is capable of tremendous achievement provided that the resistance you use is increased *gradually*, from a comfortable starting level.

For men who want to build a good physique by drug-free standards, target squatting 300 pounds (136 kilos) for 20 reps, or parallel-grip deadlifting 350 (159 kilos) for 20, with your other exercises in relative proportion. Achieving this usually requires several cycles of **Course #1**. Then for greater muscle development, target even larger poundages.

Inspiring examples

Perhaps you think that handling over 300 pounds (136 kilos) for 20 reps in the squat, or over 350 pounds (159 kilos) for 20 reps in the parallel-grip deadlift, is way out of reach for you. Not necessarily so!

Peary Rader was a very skinny young man who had struggled for 12 years on the conventional routines of his day. Then he discovered an interpretation of **Course #1**. He gradually built up to 340 pounds for 20 reps in the barbell squat.

Although I struggled with the barbell squat, because my leverages aren't favorable for squatting, I almost made the 300 x 20 mark. Then I shifted my focus to the conventional deadlift, and gradually built up to using 400 pounds (182 kilos) for 20 reps. (With hindsight, I wish I'd used the parallel-grip deadlift instead of the conventional deadlift, because that would probably have yielded more muscle growth.)

With proper application of **Course #1**, exceptional achievements really are possible.

PROCEDURE #13
Build strength over multiple set-rep formats

Here are the three groups of exercises for the purpose of specifying set-rep formats:

1) The linchpin exercises. *Each requires one work set of 20 reps.*

2) These complementary and optional exercises: bench press, parallel bar dip, chin-up, pull-up, pulldown, row, partial deadlift, shrug, overhead press, curl, and calf raise. *There's a choice of three set-rep formats for these exercises.*

3) The five remaining exercises from the pool of exercises for **Course #1**: breathing pullover, Rader chest pull, crunch, side bend, and thick-bar hold. These don't have set-rep options. *Each exercise has its own format, which will be explained later.* While the breathing pullover and the Rader chest pull aren't to be done with high intensity and progressive poundages, the other exercises are.

Here are the three set-rep formats for the second group of exercises:

a) *traditional higher-rep format*

This format—or something close to it—is the one most commonly associated with interpretations of **Course #1**. It typically has three work sets per exercise (or just one or two sets in some cases), 10 to 12 reps per set (but 15 to 20 for calves), a brief pause for one, two or three breaths between reps, about four minutes between sets of the big exercises, and about three minutes between sets of the smaller exercises. But, depending on the individual and the particular exercise, the first few reps of a set of *traditional higher-rep format* may have just a momentary pause before each, and then a brief pause for two or three breaths prior to each rep thereafter.

b) *lower-rep format*

This format typically has three work sets of 6 to 8 reps (but 10 to 12 for calves), a brief pause for one, two or three breaths between reps, about four minutes between sets of the big exercises, and about three minutes between sets of the smaller exercises.

c) *non-traditional higher-rep format*

This format typically has three work sets of 10 to 12 reps (but 15 to 20 for calves), just 60 seconds between sets, no pause between reps, and a weight reduction from set to set in order to permit the required rep count to be maintained. Once a set starts, there's no break in tension on the muscles until after the final rep has been done. This format typically yields more muscular discomfort than the other two.

The OPTIONS for scheduling the different formats

OPTION A   The *traditional higher-rep format* is employed at every workout for the second group of exercises, but the exercises it's applied to will vary if two different sets of exercises are alternated from workout to workout.

OPTION B The *lower-rep format* is employed at every workout for the second group of exercises, but the exercises it's applied to will vary if two different sets of exercises are alternated from workout to workout.

OPTION C The *traditional higher-rep format* and the *lower-rep format* are alternated workout to workout. The exercises that the two formats are applied to will vary if two different sets of exercises are alternated from workout to workout.

OPTION D The *non-traditional higher-rep format* isn't to be applied at every workout for the second group of exercises. Instead, alternate it from workout to workout with the *lower-rep format*.

The *non-traditional higher-rep format* could be alternated with the *traditional higher-rep format*, but the contrast wouldn't be as great as it is with the *lower-rep format*, and thus the latter format is probably the better complement.

When two formats are alternated from workout to workout, muscles may be better stimulated for growth than they would be if only one of those two formats was employed, at least for some bodybuilders. Furthermore, the mental and physical variety may help to sustain a high level of enthusiasm for hard training.

But, to be effective, all three formats must be very demanding once you're in *The Growth Phase*; otherwise you wouldn't be training hard enough to stimulate muscle growth.

You'll be able to use larger weights for *lower-rep* sets than *higher-rep* sets, and you'll be able to use larger weights for *traditional higher-rep* sets than *non-traditional higher-rep* sets, but you must strive to use ever-greater weights in correct form regardless of the format.

Precisely how hard you need to train in order to stimulate the muscle growth that will permit you to use ever-greater exercise poundages, you'll have to discover for yourself, but it will be much harder than how most bodybuilders train.

Recommendation

At your first cycle of **Course #1**, use the *traditional higher-rep format* at each workout for the respective exercises (namely, Option A), *or*, perhaps even better, alternate that format workout to workout with the *lower-rep* one (Option C). If your choice works well, there may be no need to try the other options. But if you feel that your initial choice wasn't well suited to you, try one of the other options at your next cycle of **Course #1**.

But the different formats must be employed in a manner that gives you the best chance of deriving the potential benefits. Excessive training must be avoided. And all the components of recuperation must be fully satisfied.

PROCEDURE #14

Use accurate weight plates

Unless you're using calibrated plates you can't be sure you're getting what each one is supposed to weigh. A bar loaded to 100 pounds may, for example, really be 102 or 98 pounds. Then if you strip that bar down and reload it to 100 using different plates, you're likely to get a different weight than before. Furthermore, the inaccuracy may be on just one side of the bar, producing an unbalanced barbell.

This is especially serious when you're moving your best weights, and when you're no longer a beginner. An unbalanced or overweight bar may ruin a set, and an underweight bar will give a false sense of progress. And when you're using small discs to increase the weight by just one pound, for example, if your big plates aren't what they seem, you can't be sure you're getting a small overall weight increase relative to the previous workout.

If you have calibrated plates available, use them exclusively. If there aren't any, try to persuade the management where you train to add a set to the gym's equipment. If you're not successful, convince the management of the importance of accurate weights, then get permission to check the plates and bars.

Ideally, discover the actual weight of each of the plates you use, and note on the plates themselves any that aren't accurate. If that's not possible, at least weigh the big discs you use so that their actual weights can be discovered. If even that's impossible, perhaps it's time to find a better gym. Otherwise, manage as best you can—discover the plates that are the worst offenders and avoid using them, or find the brand that's the most accurate and stick to that one, or use the same plates and bars every time you train.

If you know the actual weights of the plates you use, you'll know precisely what you're putting on the bar. You'll need to match equally weighted plates (or use matching combinations), or use small discs to even out discrepancies.

On the far right are the smallest plates found in most gyms—1.25 kilos (or the 2.5-pound equivalents). On the far left are spring collars, which weigh about half a pound each, and can be used as an alternative to small discs. The other plates are true little gems: 0.1, 0.25 and 0.5 kilo, and 0.125 and 0.25 pound.

Magnetic PlateMate® weights come in several sizes, including 1.25- and 0.625-pound. These are especially useful for applying to selectorized weight stacks, and fixed-weight dumbbells and barbells.

Left, a weight designed to fit on top of a selectorized weight stack. Right, a little gem pinned to the weight stack, for a small increase in resistance.

PROCEDURE #15
Use *little gems*

Build strength *gradually*. To do so, use small weight increments. This means the use of *little gems*—small discs, or alternatives, that weigh less than the 1.25 kilos or 2.5 pounds that are the smallest plates in most gyms. Fractional plates are typically quarter-, half- and one-pound discs, and 100-, 250- and 500-gram discs.

Progressing from, for example, 100 pounds to 110 in one jump, when 100 pounds was the most you could handle for eight reps, is excessive. The 110 pounds—a 10% increase in resistance—would cause a substantial drop in reps and, in most cases, lead to a deterioration of exercise technique. Even an increase to 105 pounds is excessive. But an increase to just 101 pounds may not be perceptible. Then a week or two later you may be able to increase to 102, and so on.

But few gyms have small weight plates. Most have spring collars, though, which can be used in pairs to add about one pound or half a kilogram per increment.

Ideally, get your own set of little gems—be they little discs or an alternative—and take them with you when you go to the gym.

Large washers and industrial magnets, available from some hardware stores or ironmongers, are a reduced-cost alternative to specially made small discs and magnetic plates. Find how many washers are needed to produce one pound or half a kilo, then put them on a barbell when you need an increment of just one pound or half a kilo. Another alternative, also available from some hardware stores, is chain. Have lengths cut to the weight you want—for instance, half a pound or a quarter kilo. The chains can be jammed between plates on a barbell, or hung from a weight belt for some exercises, for example.

With weight-stack machines, incremental progressive resistance can be difficult to achieve because the weight jumps between stacks are usually excessive—often 10 to 15 pounds (or 5.0 to 7.5 kilos) per unit on the stack. The solution is to attach small increments to the weight stack, provided the design of the stack permits it. Push the weight selector pin through a small weight plate and then into the stack. Alternatively, attach magnetic weight plates to the stack, or loop pieces of chain around the top of the stack. Some of these machines have purpose-made small weight pieces for slotting on top of a stack.

Plate-loaded machines permit smaller resistance increments more readily than do most weight-stack machines.

With adjustable dumbbells, remove the collars and add, for example, a pair of half-pound discs on each 'bell. If the dumbbells are fixed—the collars can't be removed—use small magnetic discs, or perhaps use wrist weights (to apply the increment to your wrists rather than to the dumbbells).

Peary Rader used to have half-pound plates "that worked well." So, he was well aware of the great value of little gems.

PROCEDURE #16

Apply *relentless progression* and *gaining momentum*

You don't need the little gems during the first part of a cycle when you're not using your current best weights. But once you've built back to just a few pounds short of your current best weights— and you're close to going into new exercise poundage territory and *The Growth Phase*—get out your little gems and *nudge* up your weights as often as possible (ideally, every week).

Then this week's 256 pounds for 20 reps in the barbell squat or parallel-grip deadlift, for example, should feel no more difficult than last week's 254; and then next week's 258 should feel no more difficult than this week's 256, and so on. Later on, perhaps drop to just a one-pound increment per week. **Course #1**, properly applied, produces *relentless progression*, and *gaining momentum*—it's the "slow cooking" way to progress, for month after month after month.

How much the increment will be during *The Growth Phase* depends on the particular exercise, how well you apply **Course #1** and the related factors, your potential for muscle and strength, and how near you are to reaching that potential. It could be two pounds or one kilo in the squat or the parallel-grip deadlift each week, and half of that in the bench press or the parallel bar dip, for example. And the increment could be halved for the final stage of a cycle.

You may argue that this method takes months to build up substantial progress in new exercise poundage territory, whereas just a few weeks at a big weekly increment will also get you there but save you several months. If you can keep a larger increment happening in correct technique for the full set-rep requirements, you'll make faster progress, but such a rate isn't possible over the long-term for drug-free, genetically typical bodybuilders. Muscle and strength are built gradually. If you try to increase the weights faster than you can build strength, your exercise technique will break down, the momentum of your training cycle will be killed, and you may not even make it back to your former best poundages, let alone exceed them. Much better to adopt the "slow-cooking" method.

Let's say that your current best bench press is three sets of eight reps with 225 pounds (102 kilos), and you're using **Course #1** as prescribed. If you progress at just one pound each week you'll have a very good chance of getting to 235 pounds after 10 weeks. Do it for a further 10 weeks and you'd be at 245 (111 kilos). Use other routines for eight months, for example, then return to **Course #1** for another dose of *relentless progression* and application of the *gaining momentum*. Although a beginner can progress at a faster rate than this (but few beginners can bench press 225 x 8), this would be terrific progress for most other bodybuilders.

There are countless bodybuilders who stay with roughly the same exercise poundages for year after year. Break out of the common rut of stagnation!

PROCEDURE #17

Earn your poundage increments

Make incrementally ever-larger exercise poundages a vital part of your training, but be a model for correct exercise technique, and consistency with rep speed, range of motion, and inter-rep and inter-set rest intervals, according to a given exercise and set-rep format.

If, for example, to permit extra weight to be added to an exercise, you rush your reps, loosen your exercise technique, or reduce your range of motion, it wouldn't be a weight increase you've earned through adaptation. It would be *sloppy training*. Don't do it. Poundage increases achieved through a loosening of form are counterfeit and don't indicate increased strength or size. In fact, such poundage increases hinder growth.

Add weight only in line with your body's adaptation to your prior training. *Earn* each increment.

But remember, it's not the weight added to an exercise that possibly causes muscle growth. The ability to handle additional poundage on a given exercise comes about only *after* the body has adapted to stimulation from previous workouts, which may include a tiny increase in muscle mass.

If you lift Mickey Mouse poundages, all you'll get is a Mickey Mouse physique.

PROCEDURE #18
Develop a strong grip

Several of the exercises in the pool from which the variations of **Course #1** are composed demand that you have a strong grip—for example, parallel-grip deadlift, partial deadlift, shrug, chin-up, pulldown, and row. If you take a number of preventive measures your grip may never seriously limit your training:

a) Don't use a thick bar for anything other than specialized grip training—use a regular-diameter bar instead.

b) Use bars with sufficient knurling. If a bar has no knurling, or barely any, it has no use for any form of deadlifting, for instance. (But excessive knurling may damage your skin.)

c) Use lifter's chalk, or rosin, on your hands.

d) The knurling on the bars you use mustn't be clogged with chalk, rosin or dirt. Use a stiff brush to remove clogging.

e) Use a reverse or mixed grip for work sets of the partial deadlift and the barbell shrug (but not for other exercises)—one hand supinated, the other pronated—and alternate which way around you have your hands from set to set.

A sixth measure doesn't produce benefits immediately—specific grip training. Grip work needs time before it pays dividends. It's included in **Course #1** as an optional extra, in the form of timed holds, preferably with a thick bar.

Few bodybuilders get even close to achieving the strength potential of their hands, often because they use grip crutches and fail to train their hands properly. Don't use wrist straps, or hooks that attach you to a bar.

Wrist straps and hooks can lead to injuries to wrists, elbows, shoulders or backs because they may enable you to lift poundages beyond what you can really manage safely.

Not only are gloves not necessary, hands can slide within them due to sweat, and the material of the gloves increases the effective thickness of the barbell, dumbbells or handles—both of which hinder the grip. Appreciate the skin-on-metal contact, and the mental focus it can provide.

If you get excessive build-up of calluses on your hands, control it by weekly use of a pumice stone.

When your grip is insufficient to hold onto a weight, that can produce proprioceptive feedback that your body as a whole can't handle that resistance, even if your musculature other than that of your hands and forearms is up to the task. You must develop a strong grip.

PROCEDURE #19
Use recommended grip aids

Chalk

The chalk commonly used in gyms is magnesium carbonate. Once you're using a weight that challenges your grip in a given exercise, use chalk on your hands. This especially applies to back exercises and upper-body pressing movements. In the latter, your grip isn't going to give out like it may in the parallel-grip deadlift, for example, but during the reps of the barbell bench press, for instance, your hands may slip outward a little unless you have chalk on them.

Experiment to find the right amount of chalk. Use too little and you won't feel much benefit, use too much and your grip may slip, but use enough and your grip will be strengthened. Rub a piece on your fingers and palms, including the area between your thumb and index finger. Rub your hands together, and blow off any excess chalk.

Don't get chalk on the floor or any other surface for feet, because chalk can act as a lubricant there, and lead to foot slippage.

Chalk isn't only for hands. For the squat, to help prevent the bar from slipping out of position, get someone to chalk your shirt where the bar is going to be positioned. If you're sweating heavily and you're going to bench press, or overhead press with your back against a high-incline bench, get someone to chalk your upper back. This may help prevent your torso from sliding on the bench during the exercise.

Chalk is commonly available from outdoor goods stores that sell mountaineering gear, or from general sporting goods stores.

When applying chalk, cover each hand, including the area on the inside of your thumb and index finger.

Rosin

Rosin powder is an alternative to chalk. Rosin may be less messy, which may make it acceptable in gyms that proscribe chalk. It's used by baseball players, specifically pitchers. Rosin may also be put on the undersides of footwear, to help prevent foot slippage on smooth surfaces.

Rosin bags are available from some sporting goods stores.

PROCEDURE #20
Keep a training logbook

Buy a purpose-designed training logbook, or get a durable notebook and design your own workout log. Then record precisely what you do in each workout, especially the weight used and reps performed for each work set. An accurate training logbook is essential so that you know exactly what you did last time, and what you need to do next time to notch up progress. And for some exercises, you may need a record of equipment set-up details.

Used properly, a training journal enforces the organization needed to get each workout right, for week after week, month after month, and year after year.

It eliminates reliance upon memory. There'll be no, "Did I parallel-grip deadlift 20 reps with 222 pounds last time, or was it 223?" Refer to your journal and see precisely what you did.

Before each set, consult your log to see what you need to load. Then double check that the poundage you've loaded is what you want. It's easy to load a bar incorrectly. Leave no room for errors that could ruin a set.

You must be honest when entering data. For example, if you did seven good reps but the eighth needed a tad of help from an assistant, don't record all eight as if they were done under your own steam. Record the ones you did alone, and perhaps note the assisted rep as a half rep.

For records to have meaning, your training conditions must be consistent. If one workout you rush between sets, then next workout you dawdle, you can't fairly compare those two sessions. If one week the parallel-grip deadlift is your first exercise, and the following week you do at the end of the workout, you can't fairly compare those two workouts. And your exercise technique must be consistently correct every time you train.

A permanent record also gives you a wealth of data to draw upon when you design future training schedules and cycles.

The spotting travesty

Don't allow a training partner to incorrectly *spot* for you. A spotter's job is to provide safety and confidence for the trainee, and should help just sufficiently to make the final rep of a set possible *if* it can't be completed solo. In special circumstances, the spotter assists at the end of a set in a planned way, to yield *forced reps*.

Some bench pressers, for example, have a "spotter" (sometimes posturing as a personal trainer) assisting on every rep of a set. Sometimes, the "spotter" seems to have more of a workout than the bencher. This is a hopeless way to bench press, or to perform any exercise. The correct poundage needs to be selected so that the set can be performed properly.

PROCEDURE #21

Get a training partner

Most bodybuilders have experienced the occasional workout when, unexpectedly, someone got involved during part or all of a training session. Someone may have spotted you on an exercise, or someone you wanted to impress was watching you, or someone may have worked in with you on a few exercises. As a result you did more reps than you normally would in a given exercise with the weight you had planned, or you did your usual reps but with more weight than you had planned. You really produced for that workout.

A good training partner can get this level of effort out of you on a regular basis, and hasten your progress.

While not essential, a serious, like-minded training partner is usually an advantage. And it's not just about getting you to train hard. A good training partner promotes training consistency, alerts you to exercise technique imperfections (which must be eliminated), and spots you. A dependable spotter will give you the confidence and security to push on when the reps get tough.

Alternate sets with your training partner.

Training with a partner is especially convenient if you're of similar strength levels, and use the same routine. What matters most, however, is that you share the same training philosophy and commitment, get along with each other, and are both punctual for workouts. You also need similar recovery abilities so that you can agree on a common training frequency.

As you get to know gym members you may find someone you could work with. Publicize your search using the gym's notice board, or newsletter if there's one. You may be able to put up a notice in other gyms in your area. And you could extend your search to any local colleges.

Don't train before you've fully recovered from your previous workout, don't perform exercises in ways that don't suit you, don't add unplanned exercises to your program, and don't abuse forced reps or other intensifiers. If you allow a training partner to encourage you to do any of these things, your progress will be impaired or perhaps ruined, and you may get injured.

But don't become dependent on a training partner. Always be able to train well by yourself. Have spells when you train alone.

Some bodybuilders work out with two or three training partners. There can be even greater solidarity, encouragement, satisfaction and progress from working out with multiple good training partners than with just one.

PROCEDURE #22

Don't wear a lifting belt

Many bodybuilders wear a lifting belt—especially while deadlifting or squatting—under the misconception that it protects them from back injuries. And some bodybuilders wear a loose-fitting lifting belt throughout their workouts.

A loose belt doesn't provide any support. And a tight belt is uncomfortable, can restrict exercise technique, increase blood pressure, and be tolerated only for short-duration sets. Powerlifters use lifting belts for singles and low-rep work.

Wearing a lifting belt can create a false sense of security that encourages the use of incorrect exercise technique.

A lifting belt is a crutch, and sometimes even a hindrance. For example, it's a hindrance for high-rep squatting and parallel-grip deadlifting.

Don't use a lifting belt. Build your own natural belt through a strong corset of muscle. Not wearing a belt helps your body to strengthen its core musculature.

Straps, wraps, squat suits, bench press shirts, and other forms of durable support gear aren't recommended either.

But a *weight belt* for attaching resistance for the parallel bar dip and the chin-up, as examples, is another matter. That type of belt is recommended.

Some elite bodybuilders, lifters and athletes can tolerate and even prosper on explosive training because they have the required robustness of joints and connective tissue. But eventually even they often pay a heavy price in terms of injuries. There's no need to take any risk with explosive training. A slower, controlled rep speed (together with correct exercise technique) is safer, and the best option for typical bodybuilders. Why risk pushing your body beyond its structural limits, and possibly suffering serious injuries, when there's a safer way to train that's highly effective?

PROCEDURE #23
Avoid excessive breath holding

During demanding exercise you won't be able to get enough air through your nose alone. Breathe through your mouth.

The common tendency, especially when training hard, is to hold your breath during the hard stage of a rep, clench your teeth, and jam your lips together. This may increase blood pressure and, at least for some people, may cause dizziness or other lightheadedness. Headaches may also result from breath holding during training. And over the long term, excessive breath holding during training may encourage varicose veins (including hemorrhoids), because of possible damage to vein walls and valves caused by elevated blood pressure.

To prevent breath holding, don't close your mouth. Keep it open—just slightly open will suffice—and your upper and lower teeth apart. It's usually when the lips are jammed together that breath holding occurs.

A common general rule for resistance training is to inhale during the negative or lowering phase of the movement (or during the brief pause between reps, if there is one), and exhale during or immediately after the positive or lifting phase. For exercises where there may be a pause for several seconds between reps, inhalation and exhalation may occur then, with an inhalation taken immediately prior to the start of the next rep.

Strength athletes who do low-rep work and limit singles, tend to hold a big breath during each rep—especially of the squat and the deadlift. The increased internal pressure this produces can be helpful during such very-high-effort reps, but singles and low reps aren't involved in **Course #1**.

Limited breath holding may be helpful on **Course #1** provided that you don't experience lightheadedness or headaches, and you don't suffer from high blood pressure.

There's a specific breathing pattern and form for the linchpin exercises. Here's the general guide: Pause sufficiently to take one or two deep breaths before each of reps 1 to 5, two or three deep breaths before each of reps 6 to 10, four or five before each of reps 11 to 15, and six to eight before each of reps 16 to 20. Breathe through your mouth as deeply as possible and fill your chest (not merely expand your abdomen).

Once you've taken your final super-duper deep breath before a rep of a linchpin exercise, *hold* it and immediately perform the next rep. The tradition for 20-rep work is to hold the final breath during both the descent *and* the ascent of the next rep. Provided you work into the 20-rep work gradually, as this book instructs, you should adapt to the breath holding and not suffer any lightheadedness or headaches. But if you do suffer lightheadedness or headaches despite your best efforts to adapt, exhale during the ascent rather than immediately after it.

Aside from breath holding, the sheer volume of breathing during 20-rep work can cause lightheadedness if you don't work into it gradually.

PROCEDURE #24
Wear appropriate footwear

Shoes with thick, spongy soles and heels may be fine for some activities, but not for when you lift weights. A spongy base won't keep your feet solidly in position. Especially when you're squatting, deadlifting or overhead pressing, if your feet move just a little, the rest of your body will, too. It doesn't have to be much movement to disrupt your control of the resistance. But don't train barefoot. Your feet need support while you train, but support of the right kind.

Function comes first in the gym. Get a sturdy pair of shoes with good grip to the floor, arch support, no more than the standard height of heel (and preferably no height difference between the sole and the heel), and which minimizes deformation when you're lifting heavy weights.

Even a small change in the size of the heel, or the relative difference between the heel and sole thicknesses, can mar your training. This especially applies to squat and deadlift variations, although a change in balance factors can have a negative effect on some other exercises, too.

Worn shoes can lead to deviations in exercise technique. Discard shoes that have unevenly or excessively worn soles or heels. Have a pair of shoes solely for gym work, so that the shoes keep their shape and condition for years. Furthermore, when you train, keep your laces tied securely; but don't tie them too tightly because that can lead to foot problems.

PROCEDURE #25

Time your workouts properly

Some people can train well first thing in the morning, but most people don't feel right for training so early. Some people like to train in the evening, but others have trouble sleeping if they train late.

Find the time of day that's practical and agreeable to you, physically and mentally. By scheduling one training day at the weekend, most people should have at least one workout a week at the optimum time of the day for them.

If practical, schedule your training so that you have enough time after each workout for more than one meal before you go to sleep. The few hours after training are especially important nutritionally, so providing two or more high-quality meals after training (and before you go to sleep) should be your target. This will get your recovery off to a good start.

To perform your best at a workout, avoid doing anything very unusual in the 24 hours or so before the session.

For example, if you usually sleep eight hours a night, but get just five the night before a workout, your training may suffer; and if you had an extraordinarily tiring day yesterday, that could mar your workout today, and it may be better to train tomorrow instead.

If there's a major event that follows shortly after a scheduled workout, and you can't get it out of your mind—for example, an important meeting, or an examination—postpone the workout. Better to wait a day or two and get in a good workout rather than stick rigidly to a schedule that results in a poor workout because you couldn't focus properly.

PROCEDURE #26
Time your pre-workout meal with care

Neither wait too long after a meal before training, nor work out too soon. Have a simple meal you can digest easily, and train about two hours afterward. Discover how much time you need for a meal to be processed enough so that you can train hard without any digestive tract discomfort or nausea.

The meal should be carbohydrate-rich, but the carbohydrates shouldn't be just simple ones. Complex carbs are needed to sustain your energy at a high level throughout your workout. Through trial and error, discover the food types, balance and quantities that will carry you through an intensive workout without any waning of energy. It may, for example, be a bowl of wholegrain pasta topped with grated cheese, a couple of baked potatoes and two scoops of cottage cheese, or a liquid meal perhaps based on a meal replacement product if you're in a time crunch. Find what works best for you.

If you have something just before you work out, even if it's an "energy drink," you may set yourself up for vomiting if you train intensively. If you ever barf during a workout, or get very close to it, consume less food before future workouts, select easier-to-digest items, and perhaps wait 30 to 60 minutes longer before training.

PROCEDURE #27
Open each workout with a general warm-up

Immediately before you train with weights, spend five to ten minutes performing some general warming up—for example, indoor cycling, brisk walking on a treadmill, stepping, skiing, rowing, or use of an elliptical or cross-trainer machine. A full-body exerciser is preferable. Do sufficient to break you into a sweat.

The older you are, and the colder it is, the more time and care you should devote to the general warm-up. In these circumstances it could involve a little more than 10 minutes of moderate-intensity work.

Here are three of the benefits of a general warm-up:

a) Making muscles more elastic and less susceptible to injury.

b) Reducing heart irregularities that may be associated with sudden exercise.

c) Priming the nervous system, and heightening coordination and mental preparedness for intensive training.

Once you're sweating and ready to lift, keep yourself warm. Stay well covered, especially between sets, and stay clear of drafts.

Do your serious stretching *after* you've finished lifting weights, not before you start. But after the general warm-up is over, do some careful and gentle stretching of any muscles that feel tight and need loosening to their normal range of movement, so that you have your normal, symmetrical flexibility.

PROCEDURE #28
Do warm-up work specific to each exercise

There are at least three reasons for warming up each exercise adequately:

a) To get liquids into your joint spaces, and to get your joints, tendons and muscles "oiled."

b) To rehearse the technique of each exercise. Do each rep carefully. Practice correct exercise form. Only once you're sure you've rehearsed the correct groove should you proceed to your work set(s). Add extra warm-up work if you feel you would benefit from more rehearsal. This especially applies to the more complicated exercises—especially the barbell squat and the parallel-grip deadlift.

c) To prime the muscles for heavy work.

But you can't do an adequate job if you use a leisurely weight. For the smaller exercises that require just one warm-up set, use about two thirds of your work-set weight. When you do multiple warm-up sets, use at least 75% of your work-set weight for the final warm-up set. For your heaviest exercises, perform multiple warm-up sets, and make the final one up to 90% of your work set(s) poundage for just a few precision reps.

If you don't warm up adequately you may find that your second work set (with the same weight as for the first one) may feel less difficult than the first one provided that you rested adequately between the first and second work sets.

You may find that a warm-up set with 90% or so of your work set weight will sometimes feel as heavy if not heavier than the first work set. This is part of preparing yourself for your heaviest sets, so don't be alarmed if your warm-up sets feel heavier than you think they should.

For **Course #1**, perform each exercise as a unit—warm-up set(s) and work set(s) for one exercise, then move to the next exercise.

Here are two warm-up examples—for the squat and the bench press:

135 pounds x 8, 210 x 8, 250 x 20

100 pounds x 8, 150 x 8, 190 x 3, 210 x 8 for 3 sets

If in doubt, it's better to do too much warm-up work than not enough. But take your full rest interval after your final warm-up set. Don't rush from the warm-up work to your work set(s).

PROCEDURE #29
Keep hydrated, and have a post-workout feed

Dehydration impairs physical performance. Regularly hydrate yourself. Sip water between sets—aim to drink at least one glass every 15 minutes of training. Use a quantity and temperature that's comfortable for your stomach. Immediately after training, have a big drink of water. Aim to drink enough water to produce at least one clear (color-free) urination shortly after training.

Within half an hour of a workout, have a liquid, easily digested, protein-rich and carbohydrate-rich feed. Consume 30 to 50 grams of protein and 60 to 100 grams of carbs, depending on your size. Within the next two hours, have a meal of solid food, or another liquid feed.

Mirror alert

Gyms commonly have mirrors throughout their training areas, which cause problems. Your reflection directly in front of you gives feedback on just one plane, which is inadequate for the major exercises, and especially for the linchpin movements. For example, you can't accurately determine your depth of motion, or your back positioning, from your reflection in a mirror in front of you. And use of a side mirror is a very bad idea because it leads to twisting of your neck and knock-on asymmetry throughout the motion, and an increased risk of injury.

Another problem with mirrors is that you develop a sense of what you're doing mostly from what you see, whereas you should know what you're doing through feel. Once you know the correct exercise technique, and have ingrained it, you should be able to perform it without visual cues from a mirror, or feedback from an assistant.

But, in the linchpin exercises, learn about your range of motion and back positioning from an assistant who observes you from side-on and provides feedback and cues. To view yourself, have an assistant tape you with a camcorder from side-on, or position a camcorder on a tripod or some alternative object. Then view the recording after you've done the exercise. How you think you did an exercise may be different to how you actually did it. If you discover errors, correct them next time. (Thereafter, a periodic check from an assistant, or from camcorder feedback, should help you to maintain correct technique.)

Never perform an exercise with your eyes closed—not even to avoid the distraction of a mirror.

PROCEDURE #30
Deal with sickness without harming your progress

Minor sickness—for instance, a cold, or a minor gastrointestinal problem—shouldn't mess up your training. Just stay out of the gym until two or three days *after* you're back to feeling 100%, and then recommence your training. Provided that no more than about 10 days have gone since you last trained, and so long as you've felt 100% for at least two or three days, you should be able to repeat your previous workout of the routine you're due to perform.

If you return to the gym before you've fully recovered, not only will you probably be unable to repeat your previous workout, you may hurt yourself in the attempt. Wait the extra day or few until you're truly 100% recovered.

If the sickness kept you out of the gym for a protracted time, you must start back with moderate weights and intensity, and take two or three weeks (or longer, if necessary) to build back to where you were before. Then return to the poundage progression scheme you were following pre-sickness.

Never train when you're sick. If you drive yourself to train hard despite being unwell, you'll lay the ground for an infection taking a firm grip on you. You may even get something so seriously embedded that you can't shake it off for a long time. It may keep returning on and off, and devastate your training.

A reminder of the overall structure of Course #1

The Revelations (Chapter 1) summarize the essential background of **Course #1**. Then come the chapters that explain the constituent elements of **Course #1**.

The Procedures (Chapter 2) cover the nuts and bolts of training, and apply to all good training routines, not just **Course #1**.

The Recuperation (Chapter 3) explains the essentials of recovery, which apply to all routines.

The Foundation Phase (Chapter 4), which is unique to **Course #1**, teaches the requirements you must satisfy before you'll be ready to start on *The Growth Phase*.

The Exercise Technique (Chapter 5) teaches the form that's required for the **Course #1** exercises, but which also applies to other routines.

The Growth Phase (Chapter 6) teaches the special training schedules that define **Course #1**.

Only when you properly apply all the constituent elements can you realize the tremendous rewards that are possible from implementing Course #1.

PROCEDURE #31

Create a *training sanctuary*

Treat your training time as *inviolable*.

Make each set perfect—perfect *technique*, perfect *control*, perfect *concentration*, perfect *effort*. This is possible on a long-term basis provided you keep your mind on one rep at a time.

The instant you're in the gym, switch off from non-training matters. Turn off your phone. Cut yourself off from the hoopla that may be taking place where you train. Ideally, train during a quiet time when there are few if any distractions. Furthermore, don't squeeze your training between two demanding out-of-the-gym activities.

Protect and respect your privacy while you train. Then make each rep a journey into *The Sanctuary*, where you're master. Without such a single-minded application you'll fall short of your best performance.

You can't enter the gym with your mind full of problems and concerns, and expect to put in a good workout. Transform yourself from your working and family persona, to your training persona.

Before you start your pre-workout, general warm-up, sit somewhere out of the way, and switch off from what's happening around you. For a few minutes, mentally go through some of the exercises that are planned for the workout. Close your eyes and imagine performing two or three reps for each exercise. Feel your muscles working. See the weights moving with control. "*Become*" each rep.

The first few times you do this you'll probably find that your mind wanders. Keep pulling it back to the focus you need. With practice it will become easier. Continue to keep your mind on your workout as you do your general warm-up work. Don't allow people or events to disrupt your focus. Then maintain your focus throughout the workout.

Each set of each workout is a chance for training perfection that can't be had again. Seize it! Each workout is a one-off chance to improve. When you train, switch off from everything else, and "become" your training.

3

Proper training provides only the stimulus for muscle growth. It's what you do out of the gym that determines whether or not you permit growth to occur.

Without fully satisfying all the components of recuperation you'll make little or no progress on Course #1 no matter how hard you may train or how well you may satisfy most of the other aspects of training.

The Recuperation
How to permit growth

The components of recuperation are *nutrition*, *sleep*, *rest in general*, and *health*.

NUTRITION

During *The Foundation Phase*, start to implement the following nutritional guidelines. But only as you're about to enter *The Growth Phase* should you boost your consumption so that you have a nutritional surplus each day.

If you currently have excess body fat, reduce it to 12 to 15% (for a man) during *The Foundation Phase*, as will be explained. If you have excess body fat, you don't have the "room" to be able to tolerate the modest but temporary increase in your body fat that's usually required if you're to build a lot of muscle on Course #1.

Once you're training hard, if you cut corners with your nutrition, your body will cut corners with its muscle-building processes. No quantity of amino acid capsules, protein powder, creatine, vitamins or any other supplement can fully compensate for insufficient healthy food.

You must increase your bodyweight if you want to build muscle. The exception is if you lose body fat while you build muscle. But very few drug-free bodybuilders—other than beginners—can do this. Most bodybuilders who have done it in a very substantial way were genetically super gifted, on drugs, or both. For drug-free, genetically typical bodybuilders, it's usually wasted effort to try to build substantial muscle while also trying to lose body fat.

Caloric intake

Calories come from the three major macronutrients—protein, fat, and carbohydrate. One gram of protein or carbohydrate yields four kilocalories, and one gram of fat yields nine kilocalories. To yield the same calories you need more than twice the weight of protein or carbohydrate as pure fat (including oil).

The energy in food that's available through digestion is usually expressed in calories, or joules. The calorie used in nutrition is actually the kilocalorie (kcal), but the terms "calorie" and "kilocalorie" are interchangeable.

Caloric requirements depend on your lean body mass, age, activity level, and goals. The fundamental nutritional rule for building muscle is to consume as many calories and nutrients as you can *without* increasing your body fat percentage appreciably, and to have meals often enough to avoid hunger.

Recall this from *The Revelations*:

> To try to maximize your recovery ability during *The Growth Phase* of **Course #1**, you must consume a sufficient surplus of calories and protein from healthy food. To try to be sure of this, accept a small but temporary increase in your body fat level. If you try to keep your gains pure muscle, you'll probably not consume enough food, and thus hinder if not prohibit muscle growth. It's best to oversupply nourishment rather than risk undersupplying it. But the oversupply doesn't mean gluttony and a heavy gain of body fat.

> Some bodybuilders who misinterpreted the nutritional component of **Course #1** consumed such an excess of food (including milk) that they gained far more fat than muscle. This is where the gains of 20 or more pounds (9+ kilos) in six to eight weeks come from. But when those gains are mostly fat, the results are disappointing because they aren't physique enhancing.

A *three-quarters/one-quarter* muscle/fat gain, or perhaps *two-thirds/one-third*, is the proportion to aim for. Then, between cycles of **Course #1**, trim the excess body fat. This is the traditional bulking-trimming strategy that's been around since long before steroids.

The idea, for example, is to "bulk up" 15 pounds (7 kilos) over a few months, with just a quarter to a third of it being body fat, then *slowly* reduce that fat in a trimming cycle to yield a net gain of about 10 to 12 pounds (4.5 to 5.5 kilos) of muscle.

Monitor your body fat so that you can quickly discover if it's increasing faster than is acceptable. For example, if your chest has increased by an inch but your waist is no more than quarter of an inch larger, that's acceptable. But if both increase by about the same amount, that's way too much fat gain—perhaps due to ineffective training and an excessive surplus of nourishment.

Measure your waist girth once a week, first thing in the morning. Use a consistent procedure, with your abs tensed, not pulled in. Your waist girth can, however, increase without your body fat increasing. Development of your lower back, obliques, and abdominals can, over time, add an inch or more of muscle to your waist girth, but that girth increase is desirable because it produces a stronger, better-developed midsection. Measure your other girths once a month.

For men, along with waist girth, measure a fat pinch taken at the midpoint between your navel and hip bone. For women, along with waist girth, take a fat pinch at a fixed spot on your hips. Either way, take the fat pinch in the same way once a week on the same day, and measure its thickness. Use your thumb and index finger to dig in deep and pinch all the subcutaneous fat, and measure the thickness with a ruler. Better, however, is the use of fat calipers. Plastic calipers are available through mail order, or some stores.

To gain muscle, there are three fundamentals to satisfy before you boost your caloric and nutritional intake to surplus level:

    a) Consume a healthy diet of nutrient-rich food.

    b) Know the baseline caloric intake that maintains your bodyweight.

    c) Be about to enter *The Growth Phase*.

During *The Foundation Phase* when your bodyweight is steady, discover your baseline caloric intake. Get a calorie ready-reckoner from a bookstore (or use www.CalorieKing.com), a weighing scale, and a measuring jug. For at least four days of typical activity, eating and drinking—perhaps two consecutive weekends—weigh all the food you eat, and measure the volume of all liquids you drink other than water. Calculate your total caloric intake each day, and find the average over the number of test days. This would be your maintenance caloric intake provided that you didn't gain or lose weight over the assessment period. But if you did gain or lose weight, make an appropriate adjustment and do the assessment again.

To get an estimate of your maintenance caloric needs, use 13 to 17 kilocalories per pound of bodyweight (or 29 to 38 per kilo). Use 13 if you're inactive other than your gym work, 15 if you're moderately active, and 17 if you're very active. For example, if you weigh 154 pounds (70 kilos), and are moderately active, your maintenance caloric needs should be about 2,310 daily (154 x 15).

Once you've done the actual assessment of your baseline caloric intake, you'll have an idea of how you compare with the estimated maintenance intake for your bodyweight. The 13 to 17 figures are only estimates, but they work for many people and may be a starting point.

When you're about to enter *The Growth Phase*, boost your caloric and nutritional intake, but do it *gradually*.

Add 200 kilocalories to your daily maintenance intake. In the aforementioned illustration you would consume 2,500 kilocalories daily—2,310 plus 200, rounded to the nearest 100. Work out a schedule of six daily meals of about 425 kilocalories each, or three larger meals and three snacks.

After three or four weeks, take your bodyweight, waist girth, and fat pinch. If you've gained weight and your fat pinch hasn't increased, add a further 200 kilocalories—six meals of about 460 kilocalories each in this illustration, or three larger meals and three snacks. Your training intensity should now be at or very close to the maximum, and the additional calories are justified provided there's no appreciable fat gain. Keep tabs on your bodyweight, waist girth, and fat pinch.

But if, after the first few weeks of the caloric boost, your fat pinch has increased, there are several possible explanations:

a) Perhaps you've miscalculated your baseline caloric requirements, consumed too many calories, and need to cut back a little.

b) Perhaps your caloric intake is fine, but you didn't stimulate any growth to convert the surplus food into muscle.

c) Perhaps you stimulated some growth but didn't provide sufficient sleep, and rest in general, to permit your body to convert the surplus food into muscle.

If you didn't gain any weight, increase your daily caloric intake by a further 200 kilocalories. Test that for a few weeks. If that still doesn't increase your bodyweight, increase your caloric intake again, and so on. Find the maximum you can consume without adding appreciable body fat.

In this way you'll find the actual caloric intake that works best for you for the time being. This is a much better way to proceed than the more common one of adopting a one-size-fits-all intake—for example, 3,500 calories—in just the hope that it will work, but risk overdoing it or even underdoing it because that particular intake is unlikely to be right for you.

Appetite is an indicator of training effectiveness. If you're applying **Course #1** properly, your appetite may take off for a day or two after each workout during *The Growth Phase*—mine used to. If yours doesn't, you're probably not applying **Course #1** properly.

On each of those higher-appetite days, spread out an additional 200 calories from nutritious food.

Each pound of new muscle needs up to about 20 additional kilocalories daily to maintain it. This is higher than the 13 to 17 estimation of kilocalories per pound of bodyweight referred to earlier. The latter is an average for bodyweight as a whole, including tissue that uses few or no calories. New muscle has a higher per-pound caloric requirement. Following every five pounds of extra muscle, boost your daily intake by about 100 kilocalories.

Stay at your gaining caloric intake *only* if you're training hard. If you back off on the effort front, back off on your caloric intake, too, or otherwise the surplus calories will be stored as body fat.

Protein

Although a protein-rich intake is essential when you're trying to build muscle, an excess of protein can't compensate for nutritional deficiencies. You need sufficient protein *and* calories, fats, carbohydrates and micronutrients.

But a sufficiency of protein, other nutrients and overall calories can build muscle *only* if sufficient rest and sleep are obtained, and muscle growth was stimulated through sufficiently intensive training.

When you're in intensive training, consume one gram of protein (mostly from animal sources) per pound of bodyweight. (But just half of that may be enough when you're not training hard.) If you're 155 pounds (70 kilos), for example, consume about 155 grams of protein a day. When you're 180 pounds (82 kilos), consume about 180 grams a day, and so on.

But when you're training at maximum intensity—when you're deep into *The Growth Phase*, you may benefit from even more protein—more like 1.25 grams per pound of bodyweight, to be sure you have enough.

Too much protein is better than not enough—excess isn't a problem provided you're healthy. But if you consume a big excess you'll probably undersupply fats or carbohydrates, and undersupply some micronutrients, and that situation may hinder your recuperation and, in turn, hinder your muscle growth.

Dietary fat

An adequate fat intake is required for muscle growth. If your overall food intake is low in fat, that will hinder muscle growth, if not prohibit it.

Not only are some fats not bad for you, they are essential. Without them you can damage your health over the long-term. Some fats are harmful, however, and should be avoided, such as margarine, refined vegetable oils, and hydrogenated oil.

Getting most of your fat intake from fish that's high in essential fatty acids (such as herring, mackerel, salmon, and sardines), along with other healthy fat from avocados, extra virgin olive oil, nuts and seeds, boiled or poached eggs (low-temperature preparation relative to frying and scrambling), and a little cod liver oil, flaxseed oil and butter, is vastly different from getting the same total quantity of fat from fried food, margarine and shortenings (hydrogenated oils), refined vegetable oils, omelettes, and scrambled eggs. Over the long-term, the different effects on health from the two alternative fat intakes may be dramatic.

In moderation, saturated fats aren't harmful like some people make them out to be. Saturated fats were an important part of traditional diets that have kept many societies healthy for generations *until* the effects of modern farming, refining, and processing were felt, including the addition of refined sugar and oils (and products containing them), refined grain products, and the use of processed vegetable oils in place of natural oils and fats.

When you build muscle it's essential that your skin is supple and resistant to stretch marks. To help keep your skin in that condition you must consume a nutrient-rich diet that's generous in essential fatty acids.

Dietary fiber

Many high-protein diets are low in dietary fiber, and wreak havoc on the elimination systems of those who follow them. To provide sufficient fiber along with many nutrients, eat these foods daily: oatmeal (or porridge), whole-grain bread and cereals, vegetables, fruit (dates, figs and prunes are rich in fiber), and perhaps legumes (soaked overnight before cooking).

If you have a digestive tract problem such as irritable bowel syndrome (IBS), *insoluble* fiber in large quantities may irritate your colon. Rich sources of insoluble fiber include whole-grain bread and cereals, dates, seeds, and beans. If you have IBS, consume more *soluble* fiber—oats, white rice, barley bread, and corn bread are rich in it, for example—and reduced quantities of insoluble fiber. But for both types of fiber to do their vital work, you must drink sufficient water.

The digestibility of grains is influenced by how they are prepared. For example, boxed breakfast cereals are usually refined and processed—to produce flakes, shapes, or even puffed grains—but the processing mars their digestibility. They also have sugar added to them and, often, unhealthy oil.

Milk

Milk in large quantities has traditionally been a mainstay in interpretations of **Course #1**. As a teenager there were periods when I drank up to a gallon of milk each day along with a lot of regular food. My caloric needs were high then, but I overdid things and made one of the classic errors—I added excessive body fat. Some people have tagged **Course #1** as "the squats and milk routine," which has encouraged excessive milk intake.

If you can digest milk, it's a convenient liquid food that's rich in protein—especially skim and semi-skim milk—but keep the consumption moderate. If you suffer from gas, bloating, or diarrhea after drinking milk, you may be lactose intolerant—your small intestine doesn't produce enough lactase, which is the enzyme needed to digest lactose. Lactose is the natural sugar found in milk, and other dairy products. Lactose intolerance is common.

Although some people don't produce enough lactase to handle even a couple of mouthfuls of milk, other people need to consume a couple of pints (or about a liter) before they exhaust their immediate production of lactase. Your tolerance of lactose may decrease as you age. But what some people may think is lactose intolerance may actually be a problem with digesting a milk protein called casein.

Dairy products including yogurt, kefir and cheese come from a process of fermenting or souring milk that partially breaks down lactose, and predigests casein. The end products may be more easily tolerated by adults who can't digest fresh milk. Unfermented butter and cream contain little casein or lactose, and can usually be tolerated even by people who have problems with casein or lactose. Soured or fermented butter and cream may be even more digestible.

As convenient as milk is, you can manage well without it. Be creative in your meal and drink design, and use fermented dairy products, and other food sources, instead of milk.

Meal planning

As a starting point for individual fine-tuning, consume 25 to 30% of your calories as fat; a sufficient percentage to supply one gram of protein (mostly from animal sources) per pound of bodyweight when in intensive training (and 1.25 grams per pound of bodyweight once you're deep into *The Growth Phase*); and the balance of your calories from carbohydrates. Within each macronutrient, get what you require from healthy, mostly unrefined food you like and can digest comfortably.

Eat at approximately three-hour intervals, such as 7:00 am, 10:00 am, 1:00 pm, 4:00 pm, 6:30 pm and 9:30 pm. Six small meals are usually more easily digested than two or three big meals, and may provide a more steady supply of nutrients. But you may have three medium-size meals and three snacks, or some other mix of meals and snacks, according to what works best for you.

When increasing your caloric intake, get the calories where you need them most. For example, if you currently eat insufficient protein, get most of your extra calories from protein-rich food; and if you currently eat a low-fat diet, add some oil-rich natural foods to your daily fare.

If consuming additional calories is difficult for you, concentrate on calorie-dense foods. For example, eat bread rather than potatoes, dried fruit and bananas rather than juicy fruits, and foods high in healthy fats rather than low in fat. And consume some liquid meals if you find getting extra calories through solid food to be a problem.

Compose a list of at least a dozen healthy meals of different sizes (and some blender drinks, too), and compute their content in terms of calories, protein, fat, and carbohydrate. Refer to a book that provides such information, or use www.CalorieKing.com.

The meals will reflect your tastes, religious and cultural background, food availability, powers of digestion, financial considerations, and any allergies or other health issues.

Some people have sensitive digestive systems, whereas others seem to be able to eat any mixture of foods without problems. Stick to the food combinations that work best for you.

Once you have a list of meals, each day put together a selection that yields your current caloric and macronutrient requirements. Here's an illustration of how one day's consumption could go.

7:00 am—oatmeal (with spices, butter and honey), boiled eggs, spoonful of flaxseed oil

10:00 am—meat and cheese sandwiches

1:00 pm—fish or chicken, cottage cheese, bread, tomato, avocado

4:00 pm—fresh fruit, dried fruit, handful of almonds (snack)

6:30 pm—fish or meat, potatoes or pasta, salad with olive oil, vegetables

9:30 pm—oatcakes or bread, boiled egg, cheese (snack)

Nuts are nutritious, but can be hard to digest because of the enzyme inhibitors they contain. Here are three ways to get nuts that are much more digestible. First, buy ready-roasted but not salted nuts. Second, roast your own nuts. (Roasting neutralizes the nuts' enzyme inhibitors.) Third, soak nuts overnight in water mixed with some salt—another way to neutralize the enzyme inhibitors. Prepare enough to last for a week or so. The soaked nuts, removed from the brine and washed, should be kept in the refrigerator so that they don't spoil.

Food quantity variation

Rather than have the same caloric intake each day, vary it somewhat but keep your *average* where it's supposed to be. For instance, suppose that your maintenance caloric intake is about 2,600 a day, and your gaining intake is about 3,000. Instead of 3,000 each day, alternate 2,800 on one day and 3,200 the next, or have two 2,800 days and then two 3,200 days; then repeat your selection, or alternate the two rotations. (In this illustration, you could have two specific 200-calorie items, or one specific 400-calorie item, that you add or remove.) This provides an *average* of 3,000 calories a day. (The variation prevents your metabolism from getting used to a steady daily intake.) While the variation probably has greatest value when trimming body fat, it may also have value when bulking. Have your higher caloric intake during the 48 hours or so immediately after a workout.

Prepare food ahead of time

Bodybuilders who pre-plan their meals, and prepare at least some of them in advance, are more likely to satisfy their nutritional needs than those who don't plan or prepare in advance. Each evening, give some thought to what you're going to eat the following day, and get properly prepared—especially for meals you're going to eat away from home. And cook large batches of food once a week (perhaps at the weekend)—for example, chicken breasts, fish cutlets, and lean hamburger patties. Refrigerate them, and use them up gradually; or freeze them in single-serving portions ready for a quick re-heat.

Pack your mid-morning meal and lunch, and take them to work—prehaps pre-prepare some healthy sandwiches. Some bodybuilders take their food to work in a small cooler.

To have good meals that can be consumed quickly when you're at work or on the move, make some of them very simple—for example, a tin of water-packed tuna and a chunk of bread, a tub of cottage cheese and a chunk of bread, or a pint of low-fat milk enriched with skim-milk powder.

Use blender drinks for liquid food, especially if you have high caloric needs, or if you need nutritious, easily consumed food on the go. Make a thermos of a blender drink at night, ready for the following day. Blend ingredients that you like and can digest easily, in quantities that are appropriate for you.

How to prepare food

Healthy food should be tasty, and enjoyable to eat. Invest the time required to prepare healthy food that you enjoy.

Baking, broiling, grilling, frying, steaming, poaching, boiling, and microwaving are the common alternatives. Avoid frying in general, other than perhaps an occasional low- to medium-heat stir-fry with extra virgin olive oil, or a little butter or non-stick cooking spray. Frying is one of the worst ways of preparing food. It damages even good food. And deep frying is especially harmful because, in addition to the high heat, unhealthy oils are invariably used and overused. And not only are unhealthy oils used in the first place, but they are often still used even after they have become rancid.

The heat used in baking, broiling and grilling can also damage food at the molecular level—but food cooked by these methods is still better than fast food or junk food, as is microwaved food.

Steaming, poaching and boiling are usually the best methods of cooking because they use the lowest temperatures—they do the least damage to food, and preserve its nutritional content.

Invest in your life

Eliminating junk food and unhealthy fast food isn't just good for your health. It's also good for recuperation from your training. Instead of nutrient-poor junk and fast food, have nutrient-rich healthy food. Avoid food that's been processed, refined, or distorted from its natural state, or contaminated with refined sugar and newfangled, processed oils.

Nutritious foods may be more costly than crud. But you have just one body to live your life in. Invest in it and you'll be more productive in everything you do, including bodybuilding, and you'll look better and feel better about yourself.

Water

Adequate water intake is essential. Merely not being thirsty doesn't mean you're properly supplied with water. Consume enough water distributed over the course of each day to produce at least four clear urinations a day (in addition to colored urinations). Until you produce that minimum, gradually increase your intake of water. Get a water filter if your tap water doesn't have a pleasant taste, or drink bottled water that tastes good. Replace sodas and soft drinks with water. Have caffeinated and alcoholic drinks in moderation only.

Keep a bottle of water handy, and have a few mouthfuls every 15 to 30 minutes, and more often if it's hot or you're exercising. Large but infrequent drinks of water increase urination but don't necessarily produce adequate hydration. Little and often is a better strategy for water consumption. Caffeine-free, herbal tea is a good source of water. Try aniseed, chamomile, fennel, ginger, mint, and peppermint. These herbal teas may also help your digestion.

Pre-workout nutrition

As noted in *Procedure #26*, neither wait too long after a meal before training, nor train too soon. Have a simple meal you can digest easily, and train about two hours afterward. Discover how much time you need for a meal to be processed enough so that you can train hard without any digestive tract discomfort or nausea. The meal should be carbohydrate-rich, but the carbohydrates shouldn't be just simple ones. Complex carbs are needed to sustain your energy at a high level throughout your workout.

Through trial and error, discover the food types, balance and quantities that will carry you through an intensive workout without any waning of energy. It may, for example, be a bowl of wholegrain pasta topped with grated cheese, a baked potato and two scoops of cottage cheese, or a liquid meal perhaps based on a meal replacement product.

Post-workout nutrition

And as noted in *Procedure #29*, within half an hour of each workout, have a liquid, easily digested, protein-rich and carbohydrate-rich feed. Consume 30 to 50 grams of protein, and 60 to 100 grams of carbohydrates, depending on your size. Within the next two hours, have a meal of solid food, or another liquid feed.

Food supplements

Nutrition is primarily about food, not supplements. Some supplements may be helpful, but buyer beware! Some food supplement companies are guilty of one or more of these outrages:

   a) They make claims that their products can't deliver.

   b) They list some fictitious ingredients and quantities.

   c) They make up research studies, select research that has nothing to do with hard-training humans, and draw on research that's based on methodology devoid of scientific credibility.

   d) They pay people for fictitious endorsements.

Anyone who claims that some food supplements work like steroids, is lying, possibly to try to persuade you to buy the supplements.

Over the years, countless food supplements have come and gone. Never look to food supplements for answers to training problems. The answers are elsewhere, although prudent use of some supplements from reputable companies may help once you have the fundamentals of training and recuperation in place.

Supplementary vitamins, minerals and essential fatty acids

Unless you're seriously deficient in nutrients, supplements can't make an immediate impact on your bodybuilding progress other than perhaps from a placebo effect. But they may benefit your health over the long-term, which could improve your recuperation and increase your training longevity. I recommend cod liver oil, flaxseed oil, and a general vitamin-and-mineral formula. (Keep flaxseed oil refrigerated once a bottle has been opened. Alternatively, grind some flax seeds and immediately consume the paste—three tablespoons of seeds are approximately equal to one tablespoon of oil, but the ground seeds have additional benefits.) Furthermore, I recommend supplementary vitamins C and E, selenium, and some other antioxidants because, in moderately high quantities, they may be helpful for long-term health.

Weight-gain and protein supplements

Although weight-gain products provide a big boost of calories, some of which come from protein, they can be difficult to digest, and their recommended dosages are often excessive. Some of these products are more accurately described as "fat-gain supplements," and contain some unhealthy ingredients.

And even expensive, "engineered" protein supplements can cause digestive-tract distress. Despite the advertising hoopla, there's no guarantee that expensive, cross-filtered, lactose-free whey with digestive enzymes and whey peptides, for example, will be easily digested.

These items are unnatural, fractionated foods. You're better off getting your calories and nutrients from healthy, natural, whole foods.

Growth hormone and testosterone elevating compounds

A number of "supplements" are claimed to produce significant elevations in growth hormone or testosterone production. Many of the claims are dishonest, and some are based on non-human studies. If any of the hormone elevations are substantial, the product concerned will soon become a prescription drug.

If you take hormone boosters for extended periods it's likely that your natural production of the hormones concerned will be impaired. And any substantial increase in hormone output beyond normal levels is potentially dangerous.

Incremental changes

Make the time to prepare good meals. Make the time to consume the regular feeds you need. Supply high-quality nourishment every day, in the right quantity for you. But if you need to make substantial changes to your dietary habits, make them incrementally. Spread them out over a few weeks.

SLEEP

If you need to be woken by someone, or by an alarm clock, or if you regularly drink coffee or tea in order to feel alert, you're almost certainly not sleeping in sufficient quantity or quality. Without sufficient sleep on a consistent basis you'll never recover optimally from your training, and thus you'll hinder if not prohibit your bodybuilding progress. Nothing can compensate for insufficient sleep.

Sleeping well also helps you to sustain a high level of desire for training, and the ability to train well. If you're tired you won't do justice to your training, and you won't stimulate much if any muscle growth no matter how good the design of your routine may be.

When you train hard and consistently, "sleeping well" usually means getting at least eight hours of quality sleep each night. And not losing sleep in the first place is better than catching up on "lost" sleep.

Although you probably like the extra active time you get from not sleeping sufficiently—to use for work, entertainment, or other purposes—you probably wouldn't be happy to trade gains in muscle growth. But that's the trade most bodybuilders make.

Sleeping well doesn't just benefit your training. It's critical for your long-term health, and your day-to-day alertness, creativity, attentiveness, and capacity to learn. What many people consider fatigue, insufficient energy, boredom, and lack of attentiveness, are the effects of a sleep debt.

As your first course of action to improve your sleep, apply these tips:

1. Establish regular sleeping habits. Going to sleep at 10:00 pm one night, and 1:00 am the next, isn't regularity. Instead, sleep from 10.30 pm to 7:00 am on a regular basis, for example.

2. Avoid napping other than on occasional days when a special event such as a nighttime flight or drive may necessitate a daytime nap. Brief periods of sleep during the day usually disrupt nighttime sleeping patterns.

3. Sleep on a comfortable mattress. It's not necessarily true that a firm mattress is best, or a soft mattress is undesirable. It depends on the individual, the mattress concerned, the base of the bed, and the body position you sleep in. It pays to invest in a good bed. Consider an adjustable bed, as it allows you to elevate your head and legs to their most comfortable positions.

4. Put blocks about three inches (seven centimeters) tall beneath the legs at the head of your bed. This slight elevation may enable gravity to help reduce brain congestion and pressure, and nasal congestion, which in turn may help reduce snoring, insomnia, sleep apnea (repeated, temporary cessation of breathing while sleeping), and headache upon waking.

5. If you usually sleep with someone, your bed should be large enough so that you don't bump into each other while sleeping. If it isn't large enough, consider getting a bigger bed, moving two beds together, or sleeping on separate beds.

6. Use a comfortable pillow. A pillow that's too thick or too thin may impair sleep, and increase the risk of neck injury while sleeping. Experiment with various pillows to find one that suits you best. You may need to change it periodically, as it loses its shape.

7. Sleep in a dark room—fit shutters or black-out curtains.

8. Put a nightlight in your bathroom so that you don't have to turn a light on if you go to the toilet during the night.

9. As much as possible, eliminate sources of noise that could disturb you. The hum from a fan of an air-conditioning unit can mask external noise, as can a device that generates "white noise."

10. If you're too warm or too cool it could disturb your sleep even if you don't feel you're too warm or too cool. Although, for example, you may think you're warm enough, you may benefit from an extra blanket. Keeping your feet warm is important. Consider wearing socks while you sleep, especially in winter.

11. If you're a shift worker, the move from one shift to another is likely to ruin your sleep patterns. The only solution may be to get off changing shifts, to provide your body with the consistency of going to sleep at a regular hour.

12. Don't take sedatives or sleeping pills, as they tend to mask sleeping problems and make them worse over the long-term, and the medication can be addictive.

13. Don't smoke. Smoking increases the likelihood of snoring, the stimulative effect of nicotine can delay falling asleep, and the addictiveness of nicotine can trigger cravings that wake smokers during the night. These are just a few of the many reasons why you shouldn't smoke.

14. Don't have a computer in your bedroom, or anything else associated with work. Maintain a work-free environment there.

15. Don't drink coffee or any other stimulant within several hours of bedtime.

16. To minimize the need to urinate during the night, finish your final meal two hours before retiring, avoid juicy fruit and vegetables at that meal, and minimize liquid consumption between then and bedtime. But have a small, high-protein, low-liquid snack just before retiring. Catch up with plenty of liquids each morning and afternoon. If despite these actions you still have to urinate more than once during the night—especially an increased need to urinate—see your doctor. In men, for example, this may be a symptom of an enlarged prostate gland. Furthermore, you may actually be awakened by sleep apnea, snoring, or another disorder, and only then do you get up to urinate.

17. Don't train late in the day. Intensive training rouses the body. Train earlier.

18. Don't have pets in your bedroom during the night. Pets will disturb your sleep if they are in the same room with you.

19. Have a small cup of chamomile tea about two hours before bedtime. Chamomile tea has long been a traditional aid for sleep. A few people, however, are allergic to chamomile.

20. A warm bath before going to bed may help prepare your body for sleep.

21. During the hour before bedtime, relax, and calm yourself. Don't watch anything on TV or at a cinema that stirs up your emotions, don't deal with financial matters, don't check your email and voice mail, don't get into any arguments, and don't tackle any complex project.

22. Immediately before sleep, read something that relaxes you.

23. Don't use alcohol as a sleep aid. Alcohol is a sedative, but while it may help you to get to sleep, it mars sleep quality. Avoid alcohol within three hours of bedtime.

When you know that it's time to get to sleep, but you're tempted to watch an extra video or TV program, stay out an extra hour or two, or chit chat for a while longer, and so on, remind yourself that your training and physique are more important than entertainment; then get to sleep on time.

Once you've caught up on your sleep debt—which may require an extra hour or two of sleep each night for a week or two, and could be timed during a vacation—just an extra 45 to 60 minutes of sleep each night relative to what you get now may be all you need to satisfy your sleep requirement. Then you'll be more alert and energetic, you'll make better bodybuilding progress, and you'll improve your health.

Eight hours sleep a night may be sufficient under normal training circumstances, but the intensive training during *The Growth Phase* may increase your sleep needs. Get whatever sleep you need.

Getting more quality sleep may not be straightforward. For many people, going to bed earlier is all that's needed. For others, quality sleep doesn't come easily. Even the general rule of sleeping until you wake naturally each morning doesn't work for many people, especially those in and beyond middle age. If you nod off easily during the day, become drowsy while driving, or need to drink a stimulant such as coffee to remain alert, you're not sleeping enough or in sufficient quality no matter how many hours you spend in bed.

Sleep disorders are common. If you snore, for example, you have a sleep disorder. Although snoring often causes amusement, it's a serious disorder. It's an indicator of health problems, some of the perceived effects of aging, and it may even lead to premature death.

If you still have problems sleeping even after applying the tips given in this section, a sleep clinic may be helpful, depending on the doctors there and their proposed solutions. Some doctors prescribe drug and surgical "solutions" that don't address the causes.

Improve your sleep, and you'll improve your recovery ability and bodybuilding progress, and your health and quality of life. You may even add years to your life.

Incremental changes

If you need to make substantial changes in your sleep-related habits, make them incrementally. Spread them out over a couple of weeks.

REST IN GENERAL

Not only do you need to sleep well each night in order to progress well on **Course #1**, you need to rest and relax as much as possible during the day. Outside of your training, minimize as much as possible activities that compete for your limited recovery reserves. Take it easy!

This especially applies during *The Growth Phase*. Eliminate cardio work. Restore it to your overall program once *The Growth Phase* is over and you shift to another training schedule.

HEALTH

Take your health seriously if you want to optimize your ability to recuperate.

Your health is the result of a composite of factors. Even if your nutrition and sleep are in good order, your health and your recuperation may be undermined by your lifestyle, working environment, relationships, emotions, and other factors. Find solutions to problems and stress. Anything that festers, will harm your health and recuperation, which in turn will mar your bodybuilding progress.

Never take good health for granted. It needs to be worked at—and not just for the sake of your bodybuilding progress.

4

"Isn't this foundation phase overkill? I want to start building muscle *now*. I've already wasted years on ineffective routines. I don't want to waste any more time."

Don't consider the delay a waste of time. It's an investment. It's essential that you complete *The Foundation Phase* in full before you start *The Growth Phase*. If you cut corners with the foundation period, you'll hinder if not ruin your opportunity to make terrific progress on Course #1.

The Foundation Phase

What you must do to be ready to implement *The Growth Phase*

To be ready to implement *The Growth Phase*, satisfy these essentials first:

1. If you have excess body fat, you don't have the "room" to be able to tolerate the modest but temporary increase in your body fat that's usually required if you're to make your best progress during *The Growth Phase*. If you currently have excess body fat, reduce it to no more than 15% (for a man), but, ideally, to just 12%. But lose it *gradually*—no faster than one pound (or half a kilo) a week. Fast weight-loss usually includes loss of muscle.

   For a man, 15% body fat usually means some visibility of a six-pack—and approximately a half-inch pinch of fat midway between the navel and a hip bone. Some indicators of body composition are inaccurate, so be sure to use an accurate method—for example, proper use of fat calipers involving multiple sites and a computation formula. (Perhaps the gym you use has the means to determine body fat accurately, or a health professional you know has, or your doctor can recommend someone.) Then thereafter, to monitor body fat changes over time fairly, use the same method of assessment.

2. When your bodyweight is steady, discover your baseline caloric intake. See page 69.

3. You must be healthy and free of physical hindrances. If you're not, take the appropriate action until you are so. See *Procedure #7* (page 40).

4. Develop suppleness. Without sufficient suppleness you won't be able to adopt correct technique in the linchpin exercises. Follow the stretching routine given in this chapter.

5. Study the exercise technique of the three linchpin exercises—barbell squat, parallel-grip deadlift, and hip-belt squat. Detailed descriptions are provided in the next chapter.

6. If you don't already perform the following three exercises, start now: incline shrug, partial deadlift, and a row, for a warm-up set and three work sets of six to eight reps. This is required to strengthen muscles that are vital for proper performance of the squat and the parallel-grip deadlift. Use the exercise technique described in the next chapter. Build up the poundages gradually.

7. Establish good nutritional habits as described in the previous chapter.

8. Establish good sleeping habits as described in the previous chapter.

9. Continue with your current exercise program but with these modifications:

   a) Reduce your training volume by 50%—halve the number of exercises, or halve the number of sets of an unchanged number of exercises. Spread that over a maximum of three workouts a week, and train each body part no more often than twice a week.

   b) After studying the next chapter, improve the technique of your exercises that are covered there. Reduce your poundages by at least 25% so that you can readily apply correct exercise technique, and then gradually rebuild your poundages as you maintain correct exercise technique at all times.

10. Based on your physical structure and training experience, and what you've learned so far from this book, you may already know whether you're better suited to the barbell squat or the parallel-grip deadlift. If it's the latter, you must have use of a parallel-grip bar. If the management of where you train won't get one, offer to provide one in return for credit against your membership to be applied once the management sees that the bar is an asset. If you're undecided about your pick of these two exercises, you'll need to test them both.

11. Once you're supple enough and know the correct exercise technique, practice the squat or the parallel-grip deadlift (or both, if you're undecided). For about three weeks, and with just a bare bar, do a few sets of 10 reps each time you're in the gym. Then change to a single

work set of 20 reps twice a week. Start very light—use a weight you could do about 40 reps with if you were pushed to (but stop at 20). Pause sufficiently to take one or two deep breaths before each of reps 1 to 5, two or three before each of reps 6 to 10, four or five before each of reps 11 to 15, and six to eight before each of reps 16 to 20. Breathe through your mouth and fill your chest (not merely expand your abdomen). Build up the poundage gradually so that after about two months on the 20s you reach a weight with which you can still comfortably get your 20 reps but have only enough slack to be able to squeeze out about 30 reps if you were pushed to.

12. Practice correct performance of the hip-belt squat, too. Perform a single work set of 20 reps twice a week. Start very light—in the same manner as described for the other linchpin exercises—and apply the same breathing format and approach to poundage progression.

Don't rush to build up your 20-rep poundage. Adapt *gradually* so that you consolidate correct exercise technique, and build physical and mental conditioning. The intensive training occurs only in *The Growth Phase*.

If you're already supple, have no more than 15% body fat (for a man), are free of physical hindrances, can perform the barbell squat, hip-belt squat and parallel-grip deadlift with correct technique, and have substantial recent experience of hard training on the incline shrug, the partial deadlift, and a row, your *Foundation Phase* will be much shorter than if, for instance, you have 25% body fat, lack suppleness, have soft-tissue hindrances in several body parts, and have little or no experience of the following: barbell squat, hip-belt squat, parallel-grip deadlift, incline shrug, and partial deadlift.

Just the beginning

The Foundation Phase isn't valuable just because it gets you ready for *The Growth Phase*. The changes it yields are of great value in themselves. Most bodybuilders have over 15% body fat, so getting it under 15% will improve their physiques. Many bodybuilders have physical hindrances that limit their training, so getting rid of them will be an important step forward. Most bodybuilders aren't supple enough, so becoming flexible will be another important step forward. Most bodybuilders don't eat or sleep well enough, so improving those areas will yield a further important step forward. And most bodybuilders aren't fully informed on exercise technique, and don't train with correct form; so improving your knowledge of correct exercise technique will be yet another important step forward.

All of these valuable changes will come from implementing *The Foundation Phase*, which is just the beginning of the overall training program taught in this book.

The Foundation Phase when you repeat *The Growth Phase*

When you use **Course #1** for the first time, action must be taken to satisfy all of *The Foundation Phase's* constituent requirements. But later, in another training cycle, when you get ready to repeat *The Growth Phase*, almost all of *The Foundation Phase's* requirements should still be in place. (This assumes that you trained on good routines in the interim, and maintained or further improved your suppleness, strength and technical proficiency, and so on.) But you'll need to reduce your body fat if it's in excess, and you'll need to invest six to eight weeks or so to reacclimatize to 20-rep work. Of course, if any of the other requirements aren't fully satisfied, you'll need to make them so. Only then will you be ready to repeat *The Growth Phase*.

Stretching routine

The best time to do your incrementally progressive stretching is immediately after you've done your bodybuilding workout. Then your muscles will be warm, and most of your joints will be lubricated with synovial fluid. This will help you to develop flexibility more quickly, reduce discomfort during the stretches, and decrease the chance of injury.

When you stretch at home, go for a brisk walk first, walk up and down a few flights of stairs, or do some easy calisthenic exercises for a few minutes.

Whenever you stretch, do it in a warm room, and keep yourself covered.

Sometimes it's necessary to stretch before a bodybuilding workout—not a full routine of progressive stretching like you do after training, but just enough to restore your current, normal, symmetrical suppleness. This would immediately follow the general warm-up work that should open every bodybuilding workout.

How to stretch

Stretching is dangerous when done incorrectly. If you try to rush your progress, you'll get hurt. Progress in flexibility at your own pace.

Never force yourself to feel pain, but you must feel tension and slight discomfort during each stretch. You'll be more flexible on some days than others, so don't expect to stretch equally well every session.

Never force a stretch yourself, never have anyone force you into a stretch, never bounce in a stretch, and don't hold your breath while you stretch.

Don't try to move right away into your current maximum flexibility for a given stretch. Work into it over several progressive stretches—each one should take you a little farther than the previous one. Then, unless otherwise specified, do a minimum of three reps of 20 to 45 seconds for each stretch.

As you hold each rep of a stretch you should feel the muscular tension diminish. Depending on the stretch, and the individual, you may need to hold a stretch for up to 45 seconds (and perhaps even longer) before you feel this slackening. The easing of tension is the signal to relax for a few seconds, then move further into the stretch in order to make the muscle(s) feel tight again. If you don't feel the tension diminish even after a hold of 45 to 60 seconds, let the stretch go for a few seconds, then slowly move into the next rep.

Stretching is a pleasure if done properly. Don't consider it a burden.

Until you're supple, stretch on three non-consecutive days per week. Later, to maintain your suppleness, just two flexibility sessions a week will suffice.

Some stretches are performed on the floor. Be careful how you get up from lying supine, or you may irritate your lower back. Don't sit up with straight knees. While on your back, bend your knees and, with your knees held above your chest, briskly roll off your back into a sitting position. Alternatively, roll to one side and, using your hands for assistance, push into a sitting position.

Progress slowly and incrementally until you reach the level of flexibility that you'll maintain. It may take you several months before you become sufficiently flexible, depending on your starting level, and your dedication to implementing the routine.

1. Calves

Stand near a support such as a door frame, or a wall. Place the balls of your feet on a book, board, or side-by-side weight plates about half an inch or one centimeter thick, and your heels on the floor. Stand upright, with straight knees, and feel the tension in your calves. You may feel more tension in one calf than the other. After the tension has eased, lean forward until you again feel tension in your calves. After the tension has eased, lean forward a little more, until you feel tension once again. Keep your heels on the floor throughout.

The stretch can also be done one foot at a time.

Develop symmetrical flexibility.

As the weeks go by, you may need to increase the thickness of the board or plates, to produce the required tension in your calves. If you feel tension behind your knees, you're overstretching or rushing the stretch, and you should ease back.

If your calves are tight, you may not need elevation to begin with. Work onto the elevation after a few weeks, as your calves increase in flexibility.

This stretch is for the calf muscle, not the Achilles tendon. Remember, tendons are almost inelastic.

2. Groin, and thigh adductors

Sit with your torso vertical and back resting against a wall. Bend your knees while keeping your feet on the floor. Put the soles of your feet against each other at a comfortable distance from your hips, and rest their outside edges on the floor. Your legs and thighs should form a rhombus.

Let gravity gently pull your knees toward the floor. You may feel tension more in one thigh than the  other. Hold for about a minute, straighten your knees, adopt the stretch again, and gravity will pull on a more supple lower body.

Keep your torso upright, with your back and head against the wall. Don't round your back, lean forward, bounce, or push on your knees. Haste or incorrect technique may produce a groin injury. You shouldn't feel tension in the area in front of your pubic bone, because that can lead to injury. If there is tension at your pubic bone, move your feet outward, and progress at a slower pace.

Develop symmetrical flexibility.

After a month or so, rest your hands on your knees for added resistance, and after a further few weeks, push downward very gently.

 To progress, bring your heels gradually closer to your hips. Progress will be slow, so be patient. But before you bring your heels closer to your pelvis, you should be able to place your outer legs flat on the floor at your current foot positioning. The trainee demonstrating this stretch should increase her flexibility at the illustrated foot positioning before moving her heels inward.

3. Hip flexors

Stand next to a stable box or bench no more than a foot or 30 centimeters tall. Bend your left knee and place your left foot flat on the top surface, with the front of your right foot on the floor about 12 inches (30 cms) behind an imaginary line drawn through the heel of your left foot. Keep both feet pointing straight ahead. Gently and slowly move forward by bending more at your left knee, just enough to produce a slight stretch at the front of your right hip. Keep the heel of your right foot flat on the floor, and your right knee straight. Hold the stretch until the tension eases. Repeat on the other side, then return to the first side once more, and so on.

If you feel the stretch more in your calf than the front of hip, you probably have your rear foot too far back.

Develop symmetrical flexibility. Take great care, and progress slowly. This stretch will involve muscles you may never have stretched before, which may currently be tight. Don't arch your back during the stretch, or bend forward at your waist.

Your torso must be straight, and upright, for the required effect on your hip flexors.

If your feet are turned outward, that will increase the involvement of your thigh adductors. Keep both feet pointing straight ahead. If the rear foot is turned inward a little, that may help focus the stretch on the hip flexors even more.

As your suppleness increases, you'll be able to bend more at your raised knee. Once you can comfortably bend your knee until its shin is vertical or slightly beyond vertical, increase the height of the elevation. Do this half an inch or a centimeter at a time—for example, put a weight plate on the box, or under it. Progress can also be made by gradually increasing the distance between the elevation and your rear foot, up to a maximum of about two feet or 60 centimeters.

Assisted stretch for the hip flexors

After at least a couple of months on the above hip-flexor stretch, add the following stretch:

Lie on a bench with your hips approximately lined up with the edge, and both knees held toward your chest. Lift your head and shoulders off the bench, and put both hands around your left upper shin. Press your lower back onto the bench, and move your right leg and thigh forward so that they hang loosely off the bench, with your right knee bent only slightly. Let gravity pull on the limb until you feel the tension ease. Repeat for the other side. Perform three stretches for each side. Keep your lower back pressed onto the bench at all times. If your lower back comes off the bench, you risk injuring your back.

You may need to elevate the bench as your flexibility increases, so that you have a greater range of motion.

Develop symmetrical flexibility.

After two months of letting gravity alone pull on your hip flexors, get some assistance. On an elevated bench—to make it easier for the assistant, and to provide sufficient range of motion for you—get in the same position as for the unassisted version. The assistant should hold your ankle with one hand and your lower thigh with the other hand, and your knee should be only slightly bent. The assistant should apply just sufficient, steady pressure to your thigh so that you feel tension in your hip flexors. Wait until the tension eases, then work the other side. Perform three stretches for each side.

Your assistant must be immediately responsive to your feedback. Never force the stretch. Keep your lower back pressed onto the bench at all times.

4. Hamstrings

Lie on your back with both feet flat on the floor, and knees bent. Straighten your left knee, and lift that limb as far from the floor as is comfortable. Keep your right foot flat on the floor, and your right knee bent—this helps to reduce rotation of your pelvis. And keep your lower back pressed against the floor. Hold your left limb at the rear of your thigh, or knee, with both hands, and pull gently. Hold this position until the tension in your hamstrings eases, then relax, and repeat. This time you should be able to pull a little further, but still keep your knee straight. Hold this position until, again, the tension eases, then relax, and repeat once more. Stretch your right hamstrings in the same manner.

The knee nearest the floor should be bent, not straight as shown here, to reduce rotation of the pelvis. Note how the lower back and the hip bones are pressed against the floor, to prevent the lower back rounding and creating just an illusion of flexible hams.

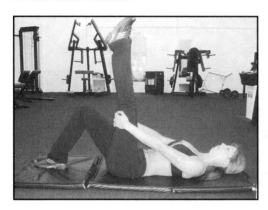

There should be no tension behind your knee—there's no hamstring muscle behind the knee. If there is tension behind your knee, reduce the tension until it's felt in your hamstrings.

To progress in flexibility, incrementally bring your leg nearer to your face. To help with this, gradually move your hands toward your feet.

For another form of control, use a towel, strap, or belt, and loop it stirrup-like over the arch of your foot, and gently pull on it. Keep your toes above your heel. Don't pull on the ball of your foot, because that would cause your calf to tighten, and mar the stretch for the hamstrings. The calf muscle should be relaxed.

The wall stretch for the hamstrings.

If this stretch is too difficult, start with the wall stretch. Lie on the floor with your heels against a wall, and knees bent a little. Position yourself close enough to the wall so that you feel slight tension in your hamstrings. Hold this position until the tension eases, then relax, and repeat. This time, straighten your knees to increase tension. To further increase tension, move your hips closer to the wall.

Develop symmetrical flexibility.

5. Buttocks

Lie on your back with your left knee bent. Put your hands over your shinbone just beneath your knee cap, or over your hamstrings just behind your knee if that's more comfortable. Pull your knee toward your chest until you feel slight tension in your left buttock. Hold that position until the tension eases. Next, without leaning to one side, pull your bent, left knee toward your right side until, again, you feel tension in your left buttock. Hold until the tension eases. Repeat on the other side, before returning to the first side. Press your lower back firmly against the floor at all times. Perform three stretches for each side. Develop symmetrical flexibility.

Especially to begin with—and this is not illustrated—you may prefer to keep your resting knee slightly bent.

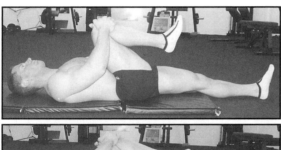

6. Spine extension

Lie prone with your arms and forearms outstretched. Pull your arms back so that your hands are alongside your head. Raise your head and shoulders sufficiently so that you can rest your forearms on the floor with your elbow joints roughly at right angles. Hold for about 20 seconds, then return to the floor. Relax for a few seconds, then repeat and hold a little longer.

Next, while still on your front, put your hands alongside your chest, or shoulders, depending on your flexibility. Then slowly push yourself up so that your back arches and your elbows straighten. Don't force it. Relax your lower body so that it sags. Hold for only a few seconds to begin with, then return your torso to the floor. Do several reps. Over a few sessions, build up the duration of how long you hold the sag, the degree of sag, and the number of reps. Work into this carefully and progressively.

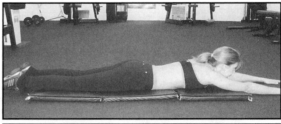

Spine extension can be great therapy for back discomfort. It can also help to prevent back pain. Done regularly, it can help maintain the natural curves of your spine, which tend to flatten with age.

This photograph shows an extended neck and an extended back. For most people, a neutral neck is the safest position during this stretch—neither flexed nor extended.

7. Quadriceps

Stand with your right hand braced on a fixed object. Bend your left knee and lift your left foot behind you. With your left hand, grab your left ankle or leg, not your foot. If you hold your foot you'll load the tendons of your toes, and mar the stretch for your quadriceps. Keep your torso vertical.

Pull on your ankle until you feel tension in your quads. And push your hips forward a little during the stretch. Hold the stretch until the tension eases, then relax. Repeat on the other side, and so on.

Develop symmetrical flexibility.

If you hold your left ankle with your right hand, the stretch is applied differently. The femur would be rotated, which would take the quadriceps out of their ideal functional alignment.

The quadriceps stretch can be done lying. Lie on your right side, with your legs, thighs, and torso in a straight line. Grab your left ankle with your left hand, and follow the same guidelines as for the standing version.

8. Shoulders and chest

Stand upright with your toes about three inches or eight centimeters from the center of a doorway. Place your hands flat against the wall or wooden frame around the doorway. Your palms should face forward, and your arms should be parallel with the floor. The elbow joint is maintained at an angle determined by the width of the doorway and the length of your arms. This is about a right angle for a typical doorway and an average-size adult. Gently and slowly lean forward, and feel the stretch in your shoulders and pectorals. Don't overstretch. Don't force your shoulders forward. As your torso leans forward, your shoulders will move forward, too. Keep your heels on the floor, and don't allow your body to sag.

To progress in flexibility as the weeks go by, step back a little from the doorway, but maintain your hand placement. Then there'll be more tension in your shoulders when you lean forward.

9. Obliques, and spinal musculature

Stand with your feet wider than hip-width apart. With your hands resting on the sides of your thighs, slowly lean to your left. Your left hand must travel down your outer thigh towards, to, or beyond your left knee, depending on your flexibility and limb lengths. Maintain that firm contact with your hand, to control the stretch. Your right hand will travel up your right thigh towards or to your right hip.

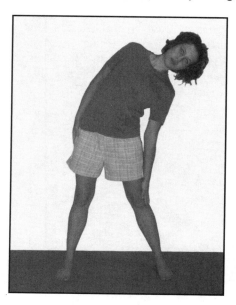

Whatever you do for one side, do the same for the other. Develop symmetrical flexibility.

This isn't just a stretch. It will also strengthen your obliques (sides of your waist), and some of your spinal musculature.

This stretch will involve muscles you may not have stretched before, and which may currently be tight.

Descend only until you feel a little tension in your right side. Hold that position until the tension eases. Then return to the upright position, and do the same to the other side. Then repeat to the left side, but this time a little farther than the first time. Then do the same for the other side, and so on. Do three reps to each side.

All movement should be lateral. Don't lean forward, or backward.

From session to session, gradually increase your range of motion.

Eventually you'll be able to reach your outer calf muscle with your leading or lower hand, and thus have a substantial range of motion. When you can do that easily, place your higher hand on your chest. That will enable you to increase the stretch effect on your side.

After you've adapted to that over a few sessions (or longer), place your higher hand on your head.

The advanced version would have your higher hand outstretched in line with your torso, for maximum effect—see the bottom right photograph on this page. Reach outward more to feel an even greater stretch.

10. Neck, back, and obliques

Sit sideways on a chair that doesn't have arms. (In a gym, you could use an adjustable bench that can be set at a high incline, to simulate a chair.) Keep your knees bent at about a right angle, and feet flat on the floor about shoulder-width apart. Rotate to your left and grab the back of the chair with both hands. This is the starting position.

Rotate your torso and neck further to your left. Gently rotate your spine. Stay upright—don't slouch—and keep your buttocks and thighs on the seat. Rotate to the point where you feel slight tension in your back, obliques, and neck. Hold until the tension eases, then return to the starting position. Pause for a few seconds, and repeat. Perform three stretches for each side.

Develop symmetrical flexibility.

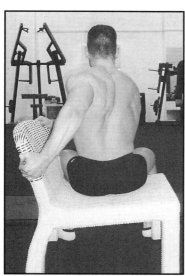

But take great care—progress slowly. This stretch will involve muscles you may never have stretched before, and which may currently be tight.

11. General lower-body stretch

A test of knee flexibility is the ability to sit on your heels while kneeling on the floor with your thighs and feet together. If you can't do this comfortably, you may not, yet, have the required flexibility or knee health to squat safely and effectively. Sit on your heels for 15 to 30 seconds, two or three times, as part of your stretching routine.

If you can't sit on your heels, perform the stretch with two or more stacked, thick books on the floor between your heels. (Your feet would have to be spaced accordingly.) Sit on the books. As your flexibility increases, incrementally reduce the height of the stack of books. It may require a few weeks of regular stretching, or longer, before you can sit on your heels. Make progress gradually.

A preparatory exercise for this stretch, is *Stretch 7.*

12. Post-workout spine stretch

After every workout (once you're training in a gym), and especially after deadlifting and squatting, gently stretch your spine, to help keep it healthy. Hang from an overhead bar, or some other support, with a shoulder-width grip, and relax your lower body so that it gently pulls on your spine, to relieve compression from your vertebrae. Bend your knees a little, then raise them a few inches, or about ten centimeters, for a better stretch. Start with ten seconds per hang, and build up over a few weeks to 30 seconds per rep.

If you have shoulder or elbow problems, be careful. The hanging could aggravate the problems. Don't relax your shoulders. Keep them tight.

Use of the traditional back extension apparatus for inversion therapy (top), and the 45-degree set-up.

Another possibility is to use bars designed for the parallel bar dip. Get in position with your elbows straight, and your shoulders tight (don't slouch), and then relax your lower body. Done correctly, you'll feel a gentle stretch in your spine. Start with ten seconds per stretch, and build up over a few weeks to 30 seconds per rep.

Rather than perform this stretch with straight legs, as illustrated, bend your knees a little, then raise them a few inches, for a better stretch.

If you have purpose-built inversion-therapy equipment available (not illustrated), use it as an alternative to the overhead bar. But don't invert yourself for longer than one minute at a time, and work into that progressively over several weeks. Longer periods of inversion may irritate your spine rather than help it.

An alternative to purpose-built inversion-therapy equipment is the use of a back extension apparatus. You can use the 45-degree apparatus, or the traditional set-up.

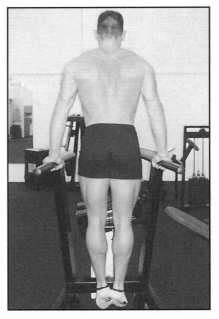

As well as one of these three spine stretches, perform *Stretch 6* after each workout.

This routine, with three reps for each stretch, can be completed in 15 to 30 minutes, depending on how long you hold each rep.

Don't consider the stretching as a burden on your time. It's an investment. When done properly, it's an injury-proofing, health-promoting and enjoyable supplement to your training program.

Symmetrical flexibility

You may find that muscles of one limb, or on one side of your torso, are less flexible than those of the opposite side. If so, perform additional reps of each relevant stretch on the less flexible side in a one-sided stretch such as *Stretch 3*; or place greater emphasis on the less flexible side in a two-sided stretch such as *Stretch 2*. Be patient, and persistent. Over time this should yield symmetrical left-right flexibility unless there are physical restrictions that require treatment.

Difficulty stretching?

If you have difficulties with these stretches, and don't progress in flexibility as the weeks go by, or don't progress symmetrically, you may have scar tissue, adhesions, or other restrictions in your muscles. These need to be treated so that your muscles can return to their normal, supple, efficient, discomfort-free operation.

As an illustration, I struggled with the quadriceps stretch—*Stretch 7*—for several years, and was never able to progress at it. Then following non-invasive, soft-tissue work to remove the restrictions in my thighs—including the removal of adhesions between my right vastus lateralis and right iliotibial band (thigh tissues)—the flexibility in my quadriceps increased instantly. Only then did the quadriceps stretch become effective. A few weeks after treatment I was able to sit on my heels, which I hadn't been able to for many years.

See *Procedure #7* (page 40) for information on soft-tissue therapy.

5

Building bigger muscles hinges on the bedrock of correct exercise technique.

Correct exercise technique is an essential component of Course #1.

You must not get injured!

The Exercise Technique

How to master the correct form of Course #1's exercises

Exercise technique isn't simple. Detailed instruction, serious study, and careful practice are required if you're to master correct exercise performance.

Exercise technique is concerned with equipment set-up, grip, stance, body positioning, and bar pathways. But for safe training, correct exercise technique must be combined with a smooth, controlled rep speed.

Although exercise technique and rep speed are separate issues, they are integral parts of safe training.

Photographs alone can't show all the details of exercise technique. Please study all of the written instructions. The photographs are for illustration purposes only. In some cases, the models didn't wear shirts so that the involved musculature or back positioning could be seen clearly. And spotters and safety set-up considerations aren't illustrated other than in a few specific photographs. When *you* train, wear a shirt, and fully attend to all safety considerations, as described in the text.

Attention readers of my earlier books

Some pages of this book—especially those in this chapter—are drawn from my earlier books. But important improvements have been made for this one (especially relative to the first editions of the other books), so please read this book as if it's the first of my works that you've come across—thoroughly, and in its entirety.

THE EXERCISES

In alphabetical order, here's the pool of exercises from which the variations of **Course #1** draw:

1. Bench press   *108*

2. Breathing pullover   *118*

3. Calf raise   *119*

4. Chin-up and pull-up   *122*

5. Crunch   *124*

6. Curl   *128*

7. Deadlift   *131*
    a) parallel-grip deadlift   *132*
    b) partial deadlift   *138*

8. Parallel bar dip   *140*

9. Press   *142*

10. Pulldown   *146*

11. Rader chest pull   *148*

12. Row   *149*

13. Shrug   *154*

14. Side bend   *156*

15. Squat   *158*
    a) barbell squat   *161*
    b) hip-belt squat   *170*

16. Thick-bar hold   *174*

Variations of the squat and the deadlift are specified above. Variations of some other exercises are included in this chapter—for example, the barbell bench press and the dumbbell bench press—but the differences between those variations aren't as substantial as those between the parallel-grip deadlift and the partial deadlift, and between the conventional squat and the hip-belt squat.

Technical accuracy

Anatomical definitions of *arm*, *forearm*, *thigh*, and *leg* are used in this book. The *arm* is the portion between the elbow and the shoulder, the *forearm* is the portion between the hand and the elbow, the *thigh* is the portion between the knee and the hip, and the *leg* is the portion between the foot and the knee.

The word *flex* is used in this book only as the opposite of *extend*, with regard to movement at a joint. *Flex* is sometimes used to mean *make muscles tense* but without movement at any joints.

A primer on anatomy

To understand the muscle involvement in each exercise you need at least a rudimentary knowledge of the names and functions of the main muscles of the human body, as outlined in this chapter. Most of the deep, hidden muscles have been excluded, however, because of the complexity of the entire system. For example, there are many deep muscles between and around the vertebrae.

Some of the exercises listed in this section—as examples of movements that involve specified musculature—aren't involved in **Course #1**.

Some of the musculature shown on the right side of each anatomy chart is different from that shown on the left. This occurs where the outer layer of muscle has been omitted in order to show some of the deeper musculature.

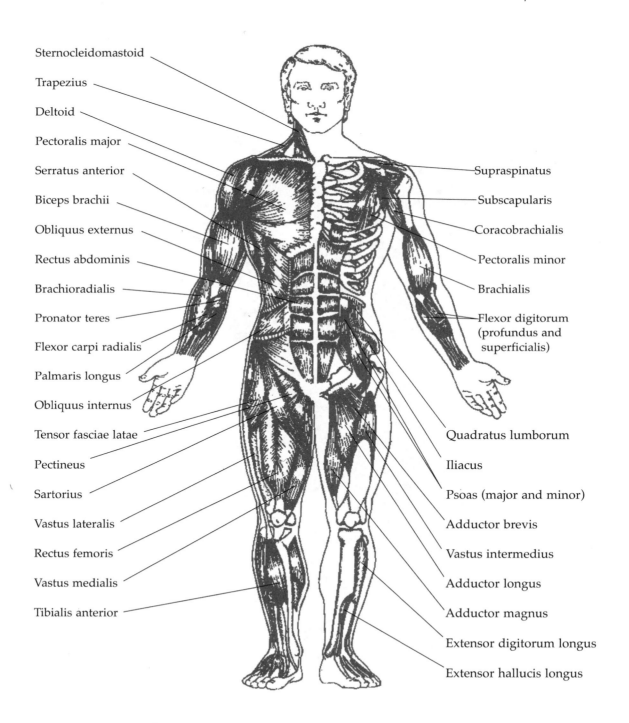

Sternocleidomastoid

Trapezius

Deltoid

Pectoralis major

Serratus anterior

Biceps brachii

Obliquus externus

Rectus abdominis

Brachioradialis

Pronator teres

Flexor carpi radialis

Palmaris longus

Obliquus internus

Tensor fasciae latae

Pectineus

Sartorius

Vastus lateralis

Rectus femoris

Vastus medialis

Tibialis anterior

Supraspinatus

Subscapularis

Coracobrachialis

Pectoralis minor

Brachialis

Flexor digitorum (profundus and superficialis)

Quadratus lumborum

Iliacus

Psoas (major and minor)

Adductor brevis

Vastus intermedius

Adductor longus

Adductor magnus

Extensor digitorum longus

Extensor hallucis longus

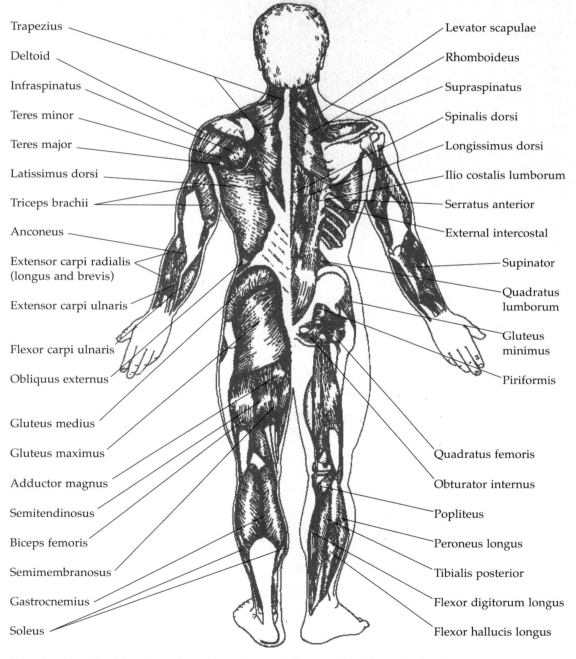

Trapezius

Deltoid

Infraspinatus

Teres minor

Teres major

Latissimus dorsi

Triceps brachii

Anconeus

Extensor carpi radialis
(longus and brevis)

Extensor carpi ulnaris

Flexor carpi ulnaris

Obliquus externus

Gluteus medius

Gluteus maximus

Adductor magnus

Semitendinosus

Biceps femoris

Semimembranosus

Gastrocnemius

Soleus

Levator scapulae

Rhomboideus

Supraspinatus

Spinalis dorsi

Longissimus dorsi

Ilio costalis lumborum

Serratus anterior

External intercostal

Supinator

Quadratus
lumborum

Gluteus
minimus

Piriformis

Quadratus femoris

Obturator internus

Popliteus

Peroneus longus

Tibialis posterior

Flexor digitorum longus

Flexor hallucis longus

Drawings by Eleni Lambrou, based on those of Chartex Products, England.

The main musculature

There are more than 600 muscles that move the skeleton and some soft tissues such as the lips and eyelids. Movement is produced by contraction and relaxation of opposing muscle groups, at joints.

Calf muscles

Group of seven posterior muscles below the knee, divided into superficial and deep groups, whose functions include extending the ankle (pointing the toes). The two main muscles are the meaty two-headed gastrocnemius and, beneath it, the soleus. The gastrocnemius connects the heel to the femur, and the soleus connects the heel to the tibia and fibula—the gastrocnemius crosses the ankle *and* knee joints, while the soleus crosses the ankle joint only. The tendons of these two muscles, together with the plantaris, fuse to form the Achilles tendon.

Exercises that work the calves are calf raises.

Other muscles below the knee

There are four anterior muscles, which move the toes and foot—the largest is the tibialis anterior, which runs alongside the tibia. And two muscles extend along the lateral surface of the fibula—peroneus longus, and peroneus brevis, which lower and evert the foot.

Hamstrings

The three muscles of the rear thigh: biceps femoris (two-headed muscle), semitendinosus, and semimembranosus. They flex the knees, and contribute to hip extension (rearward movement of the femur). The hamstrings are abbreviated to *hams*.

The primary exercise that works the hamstrings is the leg curl. Deadlifts, squats, leg press, and back extensions also work the hamstrings.

Quadriceps femoris

Group of four muscles of the frontal thigh: rectus femoris, vastus lateralis, vastus medialis, and vastus intermedius. The tendons of insertion of these muscles form the patella tendon.

The rectus femoris connects the tibia (through the patella) to the pelvis, whereas the other three connect the tibia (through the patella) to the femur. The rectus femoris flexes the femur (raises it) at the hip joint *and* extends the leg at the knee joint; the other three quadriceps muscles extend the leg only. The quadriceps are abbreviated to *quads*.

Exercises that work the quadriceps include squats, parallel-grip deadlift, and leg press.

Sartorius

The longest muscle in the body, which runs diagonally across the frontal thigh, from the proximal end of the tibia, to the outer edge of the pelvic girdle. The sartorius flexes the femur, and rotates the femur laterally.

Adductors, thigh

There are five major adductors of the femur, in the inner thigh: pectineus, adductor longus, adductor brevis, adductor magnus, and gracilis. They connect the pelvis to the femur, except for the gracilis that connects the pelvis to the tibia. They are responsible for adduction, flexion, and lateral rotation of the femur.

Squats, and the leg press, work the adductors. A wider stance increases adductor involvement.

Buttocks

The muscular masses posterior to the pelvis formed by the three gluteal muscles (*glutes*): gluteus maximus, gluteus medius, and gluteus minimus. They extend (move rearward), rotate, and abduct the femur. (A group of six smaller muscles beneath the buttocks rotates the femur laterally.)

Exercises that work the buttocks include squats, deadlifts, and leg press.

Iliopsoas

The single name for three muscles—iliacus, psoas major, psoas minor—that fuse into a single tendon on the femur. These muscles originate on the pelvis or on some of the lower vertebrae, and are hidden from view. They flex the femur, and rotate it laterally. They are called the *hip flexors*. (Another hip flexor is the rectus femoris, of the quadriceps.)

The hip flexors are worked by most abdominal exercises.

Erector spinae

Large muscles of the vertebral column—the iliocostalis, longissimus, and spinalis groups—that stabilize the spine, extend it (arch the back), and move the spine from side to side. Some of them produce rotation, too. They are abbreviated to *erectors*, and are also called the *sacrospinalis*.

Squats, deadlifts, and back extensions work the erector spinae.

Multifidii

Large muscle group deep to the erector spinae, from the sacrum to the neck, which extends and rotates the vertebral column.

The multifidus group is worked by the rotary torso, twisting crunch, and the same exercises that work the erector spinae.

Rectus abdominis

The frontal, "six-pack" muscle of the abdominal wall that connects the pelvis to the lower ribs. It compresses the abdomen, and flexes the trunk. The rectus abdominis is abbreviated to *abs*.

Exercises that work the rectus abdominis include variations of the crunch.

Obliques

The two muscles at the sides of the abdominal wall—external *and* internal abdominal oblique—that connect the ribs with the pelvis. They compress the abdomen, and flex and rotate the trunk.

Exercises that work these muscles include side bends, and crunches.

Transversus abdominis

Deep muscle of the abdominal wall, beneath the rectus abdominis, and obliques. It compresses the abdomen, and flexes the trunk.

Exercises that work this muscle include variations of the crunch.

Quadratus lumborum

Deep muscle either side of the lower spine that helps form the rear of the abdominal wall. Unlike the other muscles of the abdominal wall, the quadratus lumborum doesn't compress the abdomen; instead, it depresses the ribs. When one side acts alone, it bends the spine to the side; when the two sides act together, they extend the spine.

Exercises that work this muscle include side bends, and back extensions.

Serratus anterior

The muscle on the rib cage underneath and slightly forward of the armpit, which gives a ridged appearance on a lean body. It protracts and rotates the scapula.

Pectoralis major

The large muscle of the chest that connects the chest and clavicle to the humerus. It adducts, flexes, and medially rotates the humerus. The pectorals are abbreviated to *pecs*.

Exercises that work the pecs include bench presses, and parallel bar dips.

Pectoralis minor

The muscle beneath the pectoralis major that connects some ribs to the scapula. It protracts the scapula, and elevates the ribs.

Latissimus dorsi

The large, wing-like back muscle that connects the humerus to the lower vertebrae and pelvic girdle. It adducts, extends, and medially rotates the humerus. Abbreviated to *lat*.

Exercises that work the latissimus dorsi include the machine pullover, pulldown, and rows.

Rhomboids

The rhomboideus major and rhomboideus minor, which connect some of the upper vertebrae to the scapula. They retract and rotate the scapula.

Exercises that work the rhomboids include the pulldown, and rows.

Rotator cuff muscles

The rotator cuff is where the tendons of four small muscles in the upper back and shoulder area—supraspinatus, infraspinatus, teres minor, and subscapularis—fuse with the tissues of the shoulder joint. These muscles are involved in abduction, adduction, and rotation of the humerus.

The external rotators are usually neglected, and are worked by the L-fly.

Trapezius

The large, kite-shaped muscle that connects the skull, scapulae, clavicles, and some upper vertebrae. It retracts, elevates, depresses and rotates the scapula, and extends the head (moves it rearward). The trapezius is abbreviated to *traps*.

Exercises that work the trapezius include shrugs, rows, and the deadlift and its variations. The neck extension works the upper traps.

Sternocleidomastoid

The muscle at the sides of the neck that connects the sternum and clavicles to the skull. Acting together, both sides of the sterno-cleidomastoid flex the head and neck; when acting separately, each muscle produces rotation and lateral flexion.

The forward flexion on the four-way neck machine is the preferred exercise for this muscle.

Deltoid

The shoulder cap muscle. It abducts, flexes, extends, and rotates the humerus. It has three heads: anterior, medial, and posterior. The deltoids are abbreviated to *delts*.

Exercises that work the deltoids include the dumbbell press, barbell press, and lateral raise.

Biceps brachii

The two-headed muscle (long, and short heads) of the front or anterior surface of the arm, which connects the upper scapula to the radius and forearm muscle, and flexes the forearm and thus the elbow joint, and supinates the forearm. The biceps are abbreviated to *bis*.

Exercises that work the biceps include curls, pulldown, and rows.

Brachialis

The muscle of the front of the arm beneath the biceps, which connects the humerus to the ulna, and flexes the forearm and elbow joint.

Exercises that work the brachialis include curls, pulldown, and rows.

Triceps brachii

The three-headed muscle (long, medial, and lateral heads) on the rear or posterior surface of the arm, which connects the humerus and scapula to the ulna, and extends the forearm (and the elbow joint). Just the long head of the triceps adducts the arm. The triceps are abbreviated to *tris*.

Exercises that work the triceps include bench presses, presses, parallel bar dips, and pushdown.

Forearms

The anterior surface (palm side) has eight muscles spread over three layers, most of which are involved in flexing the wrist and fingers. The posterior surface has ten muscles spread over two layers, involved in extending the wrist and moving the fingers.

Timed hold, deadlifts, shrugs, grippers, rows, pulldown, and finger extension work the forearms, along with all exercises that work the grip.

The four main grips

Pronated grip

When your hands are at your sides, a pronated grip has your knuckles facing to the front, and palms facing to the rear. When your hands are overhead, the grip has your knuckles facing to the rear, and palms to the front.

Supinated grip

When your hands are at your sides, a supinated grip has your knuckles facing to the rear, and palms facing to the front. When your hands are overhead, the supinated grip has your knuckles facing to the front, and your palms facing to the rear.

Parallel grip

A grip that has the palms parallel to each other.

Reverse grip

A grip where a bar is held with one hand pronated and the other supinated. It's a specialized grip for a small number of exercises, such as the deadlift and the shrug. The reverse grip strengthens the hold on the bar largely because it prevents the bar rolling in the hands. It's also called an *alternating grip*, or a *mixed grip*.

Four different grips: left, pronated grip (two views); middle, supinated grip (two views); top right, parallel grip; bottom right, mixed or reverse grip.

BENCH PRESS

Four forms of the bench press will be described:

barbell bench press
dumbbell bench press
incline barbell bench press
incline dumbbell bench press

A combination bench-and-weight-stands unit, but without spotter bars. An assistant must be used as a spotter with this type of unit. There's a raised platform here for the spotter to stand on, for easier handling of the barbell by the spotter. An unloaded barbell is shown across the unit's upper bar saddles.

Barbell bench press

Main muscles worked

pectorals, deltoids, triceps

Capsule description

lie on your back, bar in your hands, arms vertical, elbows locked; lower the bar to your chest, then push it up

Set-up

This exercise is done supine, lying on your back on a horizontal bench. Use a straight barbell, not one with bends or cambers in it. Bench press inside a four-post power rack with pins and saddles correctly positioned, and securely in place.

Alternatively, bench press between sturdy squat stands together with spotter (or safety) bars or racks, or use a half rack, or use a combination bench-and-weight-stands unit together with spotter bars. Some bench-and-stands units have built-in, adjustable spotter bars. Set the safety bars at the appropriate height, and position yourself on the bench so you won't miss the safety bars if you need to set the barbell on them.

If there are no spotter or safety bars to prevent the bar from getting stuck on your chest if you fail on a rep, you must have an alert and strong spotter in attendance.

Center a sturdy, stable bench between the weight supports. In a power rack, if possible, mark where the bench should be, to be centered. Use a tape measure to ensure correct centering. The rack and bench should be level—have them checked, and corrected if necessary.

Depending on the bench press unit you use, the bar saddles may be adjustable. Position them neither too high, nor too low.

Positioning on the bench

Position yourself on the bench so that you won't hit the uprights of the rack or stands with the bar during the bench press ascent, but also so that you minimize the horizontal movement of the bar during the unracking and racking of the bar. The bar, when racked, may, for example, be directly above your nose. The set-up varies according to individual body structure, height of the bar holders, and depth of the saddles. Experiment with a bare bar, to find what works best for you. Make a note of where your eyes are, relative to the bar, when you're on the bench with the bar in the saddles, ready to unrack the bar to start a set.

Lie on the bench with your feet, hips, back, and head all in position. Your heels should be on an imaginary vertical line drawn from your knees, or slightly in front of it. If your heels are behind this line (that is, pulled toward your pelvis) that will lead to exaggerated arching of your lower spine. Avoid that. Although some arching in the lower spine is normal, don't exaggerate it. Some trainees exaggerate the arch, to raise their chests as much as possible in order to reduce the distance the bar has to move before it touches their chests, to increase the weights they use. This technique has injured many trainees.

Establish a strong base, with your feet flat on the floor wider than shoulder width. Don't place your feet close together on the floor, and don't place them on the bench in any manner—both placements would reduce your stability. Never lift your heels off the floor during the bench press. If you have short lower limbs and can't keep your feet flat on the floor, raise your feet a few inches using low blocks, or plates stacked smooth side up.

Set the rack's pins, or whatever safety bars you use, an inch (two-and-a-half centimeters) below the height of your inflated chest when you're in position on the bench. A length of hose or tubing may be put over each safety bar, to soften contact with the barbell. If you fail on a rep, lower the bar to your chest, exhale, and set the bar on the supports.

Grip

While the bar is at the line of your lower pecs, your hand spacing should put your forearms in a vertical position when viewed (by an assistant) from the side and from your feet. Your elbows should be directly under your wrists. Adult men should use a grip with 21 inches or 53 centimeters between their index fingers as a starting point. Women should use a grip four inches or ten centimeters narrower.

 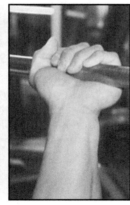

The thumbless or false grip on the left, and the correct grip on the right.

Fine-tune from there to find the grip that gives you the proper forearm and elbow positioning. Once you find your optimum grip, have someone

measure the distance between your index fingers, and make a written note of it.

Don't use a thumbless grip, because it reduces your control over the bar. Wrap your thumbs under and around the bar.

Grip with your hands equidistant from the bar's center. Be sure you're not even a fraction of an inch off center. Before a set, know precisely where your hands should be—use a tape measure if necessary.

If the back of your hands, wrists and forearms is in a straight line during the bench press, or any pressing movement, the bar will fall out of your hands. Your hands must move rearward sufficiently so that you can grip the bar securely. But don't allow the bar to extend your hands to the maximum, because that can mar your lifting technique, and injure your wrists. (The bar should be gripped firmly, because the slacker the grip, the less the actions of the flexors on the palm side of the forearm, which translates to less muscular counteraction to the rearward bending.) Once the bar is in a secure position in your hands, keep your wrists rigid for the duration of each set.

Performance

Get in position on the bench, hands in place on the bar, with a spotter or training partner standing directly behind you. Have the spotter or training partner give you a hand-off as you fully straighten and lock out your elbows. Pause until the bar is steady above your chest, inhale fully to fill your chest, pull your shoulders back, then immediately lower the bar under control. The full inhalation, and pulling back of the shoulders, help to produce the required tight, full chest. (Your chest mustn't collapse during the bench press.) Take two to three seconds for the descent.

Lower the bar to a point below your nipples, at about the bottom line of your pectoral muscles. Find the precise point that's best for you. When the bar is on your chest, your forearms should be vertical when viewed from the side *and* the front (or the rear, depending on where the viewer is). If they aren't, your hand spacing is incorrect.

Never bounce the bar off your chest. Touch your chest with the bar, pause there for one second, then push it up. Stay tight at the bottom with a full chest and firm grip—don't relax.

The ascent of the bar should be vertical, or slightly diagonal if that feels more natural—with just three or four inches of horizontal movement toward your head. Try both, and see which works best for you.

Keep your forearms as vertical as possible during the ascent. Do this through keeping your elbows directly beneath your wrists.

To maintain the required tight, full chest, don't exhale until during the top half of the ascent, or until you've completed the ascent.

The hand-off to start a bench press set (top), the top position prior to the descent (middle), and the bottom position at the lower pectoral line (above).

Check yourself on a video recording, or have someone watch you from the side. What you may think, for example, is a vertical movement, may be angled slightly toward your feet. Practice until you can keep the bar moving correctly.

The ascent, just like the descent, should be symmetrical. The bar shouldn't tip to one side, both hands should move in unison, and you shouldn't take more weight on one side of your body than the other.

After locking out the bar, pause for a second or until the bar is stationary, inhale fully, pull your shoulders back, then again lower the bar slowly to the correct position on your lower chest.

Common errors—DANGER

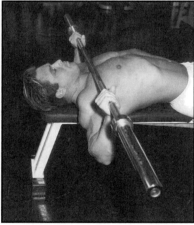

Two of the most common bench pressing errors. Top, exaggeration of the arch in the lower spine—from having the feet behind the knees, and not keeping the feet flat on the floor. This has injured the lower backs of many bodybuilders. Above, bench pressing to the upper chest. This has injured the shoulders of many bodybuilders.

Other tips

Keep your head flat on the bench. Never turn your head while you're lifting or lowering the bar. If you do, the bar may tip, and then your groove would be marred, and you could injure yourself.

Don't drive your head back into the bench, or otherwise you'll risk injury to your neck.

Use chalk or rosin on your hands to improve your grip on the bar, but keep the knurling clean.

Once you've learned correct technique in the bench press, drill yourself on a fixed set-up and approach-to-the-bar procedure.

Once you've mastered bench pressing technique, give 100% attention to ensure that you deliver correct technique on every rep. Even a slight slip of concentration can lead to lowering the bar slightly out of position, or having one hand out of step with the other. Either of these will ruin your groove. This will make the weight feel heavier, make your reps harder, and risk injury.

Spotting

A hand-off to get the bar out of the saddles to start the set, is the first function of a spotter. During a set, as soon as the bar stalls or tips, or one hand gets forward of the other, the spotter must act to prevent the rep deteriorating further and causing injury.

The spotter must use both hands and provide sufficient assistance to keep the bar horizontal and moving correctly, centered above the lifter.

Even if the spotter doesn't need to assist during a rep, he should guide the bar back into the weight saddles after the final rep. At the end of a hard set of bench presses, you'll be tired. Without a guiding pair of hands on the bar from a spotter, you may miss getting the bar into the weight saddles. Throughout spotting, the spotter mustn't round his back, to protect *his* back.

How a single assistant should spot the bench press. This bench press unit has a platform for the spotter to stand on, for more efficient spotting.

The spotting travesty

Some bench pressers have a "spotter" (sometimes posturing as a personal trainer) assisting the trainee on the first rep of a set and every rep thereafter—usually because there's more weight on the bar than the bencher can currently handle properly. Sometimes, the "spotter" seems to have more of a workout than the bencher. This is a hopeless way to bench press, or to perform any exercise.

A spotter's job is to provide safety and confidence for the trainee, and should help just sufficiently to make the final rep of a set possible if it can't be completed solo. In special circumstances, the spotter assists on a couple of reps at the end of a set in a planned arrangement to yield *forced reps*.

Two pectoralis muscles

"Pectorals" and "pecs" refer to the pectoralis major—the large, flat muscle on each side of the upper rib cage. There's also the pectoralis *minor*, a much smaller muscle beneath the pectoralis major.

The pec minor protracts the scapula forward, as when a person reaches for something. The pec major is a prime mover of the humerus, as when a person bench presses, for example.

The pec minor isn't the upper pec, and doesn't make any significant contribution to chest development. What's considered to be the upper pec is the clavicular portion of the pectoralis major.

Dumbbell bench press

Main muscles worked

pectorals, deltoids, triceps

Capsule description

lie on your back, dumbbells in your hands, arms vertical, elbows locked; lower the dumbbells to your chest, then push them up

The bench press can also be done with dumbbells, again from a supine position on a horizontal bench. Once the 'bells are in pressing position, the technique is similar to the barbell version.

There are some advantages of the dumbbell version. First, provided there are suitable dumbbells available, you can probably dumbbell bench press whenever you want, and avoid having to wait your turn at the barbell bench press stations. Second, the dumbbell bench press doesn't require a power rack or other safety set-up, but a spotter is still required. Third, the 'bells provide more potential than a barbell does for optimizing hand and wrist positioning—a barbell fixes the hands into a pronated position.

The disadvantages of the dumbbell bench press are several. First, getting two heavy dumbbells into and out of position is difficult—and potentially dangerous—unless you have at least one competent assistant. Second, there's a greater chance of overstretching on the lowering phase than with a barbell. Third, balance is tricky, and if control is lost over one or both dumbbells during a set, you could sustain serious injury. In addition, the floor and equipment could be damaged if the dumbbells are dropped. Of course, the barbell bench press can be dangerous unless done correctly, inside a power rack with pins properly positioned.

Clockwise, from the bottom left, how to get into position, without assistance, for the dumbbell bench press, and the first ascent of the set.

Performance

To get into position for dumbbell bench pressing, have a spotter hand you the 'bells one at a time while you're in position on a bench (as you would be for the barbell bench press).

Alternatively, get the dumbbells into position by yourself. Sit on the end of a bench with the 'bells held vertically on your thighs. Center your hands on the handles. Keep your elbows bent, chin on your chest, back rounded, and, with a thrust on the 'bells from your thighs, roll back on the bench and position your feet properly, like for the barbell bench press. With your forearms vertical, and hands lined up with your lower pecs, inhale fully to fill your chest, pull your shoulders back, and immediately begin pressing.

Press in a similar pathway as in the barbell version. Keep the 'bells moving in tandem, as if they were

From the top, the last descent of a set of dumbbell benches, and the return to the seated position.

linked. Don't let them drift outward from your torso, or let one get ahead of the other.

With dumbbells you don't have to hold your hands as if holding a barbell. Use a parallel grip, or one somewhere in between that and the barbell-style pronated grip. You can change your wrist positioning during the course of each rep.

If the back of your hands, wrists and forearms is in a straight line during the dumbbell bench press, or any pressing movement, the dumbbells will fall out of your hands. Your hands must extend rearward sufficiently so that you can grip the dumbbells securely. But don't allow the dumbbells to extend your hands to the maximum, because that can mar your lifting technique, and injure your wrists. (The dumbbells should be gripped firmly, because the slacker the grip, the less the actions of the flexors on the palm side of the forearm, which translates to less of a muscular counteraction to the rearward bending.) Once the dumbbells are in a secure position in your hands, keep your wrists rigid for the duration of each set.

Don't seek an exaggerated range of motion. Keep your hands near to the spacing that was recommended for the barbell bench press. Don't use a wider grip so that you can get your hands lower at the bottom of the exercise. Descend to a point no deeper than you would on a barbell bench press. Pause at the bottom for a second, then ascend smoothly, under control. Pause for a second at the top, or until the dumbbells are stationary, then smoothly perform the next rep.

Your control may be poor at first, but with practice you'll develop control over the dumbbells.

Follow the same breathing pattern that was prescribed for the barbell bench press.

Adding weight

Fixed-weight dumbbells usually increase in increments of 5 pounds (or 2.5 kilos). Going up in dumbbells usually means a total increase of 10 pounds, which is large. Stick with a pair of dumbbells until you can comfortably do several reps more than your target count, before going up in weight the next time you dumbbell bench press.

If you use adjustable dumbbells, you can use smaller increments than 5 pounds provided you have small discs. Even if you use fixed-weight dumbbells, you can attach two small discs to each dumbbell. Use strong adhesive tape and ensure that the discs are securely attached. Over time, build up to the weight of the next pair of fixed-weight dumbbells. To ensure proper balance, attach the small discs in pairs to each dumbbell, one at each end. Better to use magnetic small plates.

Spotting

A spotter should crouch behind your head, ready to provide assistance. One hand should apply force under each elbow. But this is strictly for assisting a lifter to get a tough rep up in correct technique. A single person can't simultaneously take a pair of 'bells from someone who fails on a rep. Two spotters are needed, then.

Don't push this exercise to failure. Even when you're training hard, stop this exercise one rep short of failure, so you don't risk losing control. Losing control could cost you an injury. Even an alert spotter may not be able to prevent loss of control of both dumbbells.

A spotter, or better still two spotters, can take the dumbbells off you at the end of a set. Alternatively, get off the bench while holding the dumbbells. Here's how, as illustrated on the left: Lower the 'bells to your lower torso, keep your forearms, arms, shoulders and chest tight, and lift your bent knees as high as you can. With the 'bells touching your thighs, and your chin on your chest, immediately throw your feet forward and roll into a seated position. This is especially easy to do if a spotter places his hands under your shoulders and helps you to roll up.

A spotter should be careful not to round his back while spotting you, to protect *his* back.

Incline barbell bench press

Main muscles worked

pectorals, deltoids, triceps

the incline bench press may place more stress on the upper pectorals (clavicular head) than does the horizontal, supine version

Capsule description

lie on your back on an incline bench, bar overhead; lower bar to your chest, then push it up

An incline bench press unit, with built-in (black) adjustable safety bars. An unloaded barbell is shown resting across the unit's bar saddles.

Set-up

Use a heavy-duty, adjustable bench, preferably one that has an adjustment for tilting the seat—to prevent the user slipping out of position. Use a low-incline bench that has an angle no greater than 30 degrees with the horizontal. Most incline benches are set too upright for this exercise.

Ideally, do the exercise in a power rack, with pins properly positioned for safety. Alternatively, do the exercise in a purpose-built, incline bench press unit. If you do the exercise outside the safety of a power rack, have a spotter standing by in case you get stuck on a rep. The spotter is also needed to help you to get the bar out of the saddles safely, and return it to the saddles after the set is over.

Grip, and bar placement

Start with the same grip as in the standard bench press, and fine-tune if necessary. Don't use a thumbless grip, but wrap your thumbs around the bar properly. Furthermore, as in the bench press, your hands must extend rearward sufficiently so that you can grip the bar securely. But don't allow the bar to extend your hands to the maximum, because that can mar your lifting technique, and injure your wrists. Grip the bar firmly, to help keep your wrists in the right position. Once the bar is in a secure position in your hands, keep your wrists rigid for the duration of each set.

Rather than wonder where to place the bar on your chest at the bottom of the incline press, look at it in terms of your forearms and arms. Your forearms should be vertical at the bottom—vertical when viewed from the side *and* from the front. (Get the help of an assistant.) At that position your arms should be at about a 45 to 60 degree angle to your rib cage. The precise angle will vary from individual to individual, largely because of forearm and arm lengths, and torso girth variations. Get your forearms in the right position, and you should automatically find the ideal placement of the bar on your chest.

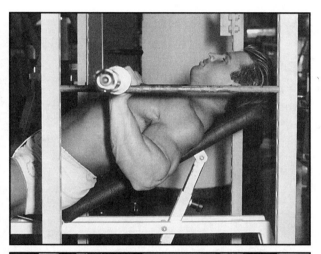

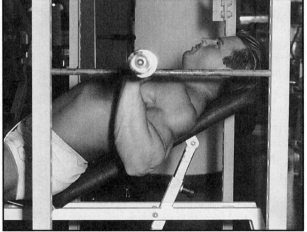

Top, hand spacing a little too wide. Bottom, better hand spacing, elbows directly beneath the wrists.

Don't lower the bar as low on your chest as in the regular bench press. Because of the inclination of the bench, a low position of the bar on your chest would lead to excessive and unsafe extension of your shoulders. Nor should you lower the bar to your neck or clavicles—that positioning is also dangerous for your shoulders.

Your forearms should be vertical when viewed from the side. Top photograph, bar too low on the chest, which produces excessive shoulder extension. Above, correct positioning.

Performance

Position yourself on the incline bench, and plant your feet solidly on the floor, or on a foot brace if one is provided. Keep your feet fixed in position. Don't lift or shuffle them. Your feet should be flat on the floor, wider than shoulder width. Feet positioned close together reduce stability.

With a hand-off, take the barbell out of the stands. Straighten your elbows, pause for a second, then lower the bar under control. Touch your chest at the position explained earlier, and pause for a second. Keep yourself tight during the pause, with your abdominal muscles, buttocks, and lats contracted. Then smoothly press up and slightly back. After straightening your elbows, pause for a second, or until the bar is stationary, then lower it for the next rep.

Follow the same breathing pattern that was prescribed for the barbell bench press.

Spotting

See *Bench press*. The same guidelines apply to spotting the incline barbell press. In addition, the spotter needs to be elevated, to apply assistance with least difficulty. For the spotter to avoid injury, he must maintain a slightly hollow lower spine, and get as close to the trainee as possible.

Caution

When you incline press, don't exaggerate the hollow in your lower spine. With your feet flat on the floor, keep your heels directly beneath or slightly in front of an imaginary vertical line drawn through the middle of your knees. If your feet are behind your knees, the arch will probably be exaggerated, and the risk of injury increased.

But, if the seat of the bench is too high and can't be adjusted, or if you have short lower limbs, this strategy won't work well. A non-slip, low block or platform under each foot will be required. A wide single platform would also do the job. The wider your feet, the greater your stability.

When preparing to unrack the bar from behind your head to get ready for the first rep of a set of the incline barbell bench press, don't draw your elbows behind your wrists, or even in line with your wrists. If your elbows are drawn back, then as you unrack the bar the stress on your shoulders will be increased greatly, and unnecessarily. Keep your elbows in front of your wrists while you unrack the bar. But provided you use a spotter, you won't have to take much of the strain from unracking the bar while getting set up for the first rep.

Incline dumbbell bench press

Main muscles worked

pectorals, deltoids, triceps

the incline bench press may place more stress on the upper pectorals (clavicular head) than does the horizontal, supine version

Capsule description

lie on your back on an incline bench, with the dumbbells overhead; lower the dumbbells to your chest, then push them up

The incline bench press can also be done with dumbbells. Once the dumbbells are in position for pressing, the technique is basically the same as in the barbell version.

A big advantage of dumbbells is that you can use whatever wrist positioning is most comfortable, rather than have your wrists fixed by a barbell into a pronated position. But there are handling difficulties getting the 'bells into position. See *Dumbbell bench press* for the main pros and cons of dumbbell bench pressing.

As in other pressing movements, your hands must extend rearward sufficiently so that you can grip the dumbbells securely. But don't allow the dumbbells to extend your hands to the maximum, because that can mar your lifting technique, and injure your wrists. Grip the bar firmly, to help keep your wrists in the right position. Once the dumbbells are in a secure position in your hands, keep your wrists rigid for the duration of each set.

To perform the dumbbell incline bench press, you require a method for getting the dumbbells into position ready for pressing. See *Dumbbell bench press* for how to do this.

During the pressing, pay special attention to keeping the dumbbells from drifting out to the sides, go no deeper than in the barbell version, and keep the 'bells moving in tandem. You'll probably need a few workouts to get the feel for the exercise, and to find the wrist positioning that suits you best.

Follow the same breathing pattern that was prescribed for the barbell bench press.

See *Dumbbell bench press* for tips on how to progress gradually from one pair of fixed-weight dumbbells, to the next.

Spotting

See *Dumbbell bench press*. The same guidelines apply to spotting the incline dumbbell bench press, but in the latter there's no need for the spotter to crouch.

With any type of dumbbell pressing, key markers of technique deterioration are the 'bells drifting out to the sides, and one hand getting above, in front of, or to the rear of the other. Don't push this exercise to failure. Stop a rep short of failure, so that you don't risk losing control of the 'bells.

Caution

Don't exaggerate the hollow in your lower spine. See *Incline barbell bench press*.

Periodically, use a camcorder to record your exercise technique, for analysis later. A camcorder can be an outstanding tool to help you improve your exercise technique.

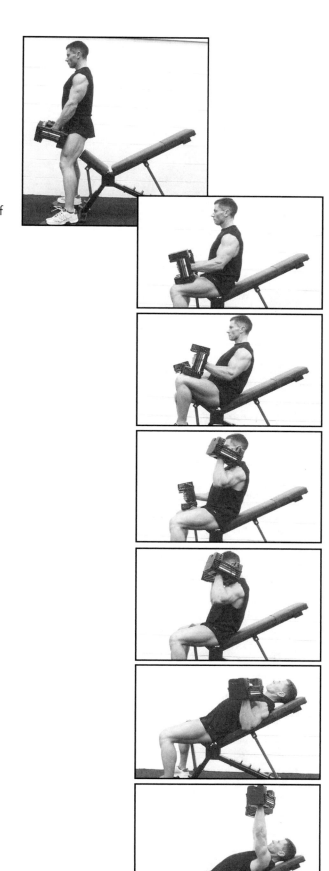

BREATHING PULLOVER

Main structure worked

rib cage

Capsule description

move resistance to and from behind your head, with straight elbows

This is a stretching and forced breathing exercise that may enlarge your rib cage, deepen your chest, and help to improve your posture. It—or its alternative, the *Rader chest pull*—is a mainstay of **Course #1**.

It may be especially effective for teenagers, and trainees in their early twenties, but is worth a try at any age. There's no science to confirm this, however. I believe the breathing pullover helped me, and other people have reported benefits, too.

Use no more than 10 pounds (or 5 kilos) to begin with—a pair of small dumbbells, a single dumbbell, or a barbell plate. (The pullover machine shouldn't be used for the breathing pullover.) After a few months you may increase to 15 pounds (or 7.5 kilos), and later to 20 pounds (or 10 kilos) if you're a large man, but no more. Don't use progressive resistance in this exercise. The use of heavy weights will defeat the purpose of the exercise, as well as risk harm to your shoulders. If in doubt over which weight to use here, select the lighter one.

Hold the resistance and lie lengthwise on a bench, not across it. Keep your feet on the bench. This prevents excessive arching of your back, and excessive stretching of your abdominal wall. Hold the resistance above your upper chest, with straight elbows. Take a shoulder-width grip, or closer if you're using a single dumbbell or weight plate. Keep your elbows stiff and straight, and slowly lower the bar as you simultaneously inhale as deeply as possible. Don't inhale in one gulp, but in a steady stream. Spread your ribs as much as possible. Lower your arms until they are parallel or just slightly below parallel with the floor. Don't go down as deep as possible. At the bottom position, take an extra gulp of air. Pause for a second, then return to the starting position, simultaneously exhaling. Repeat for at least 15 slow reps. Focus on stretching your rib cage.

Experiment with a different positioning. Do the exercise with your head just off the end of the bench, as illustrated. This may produce a better effect on your rib cage.

Keeping your elbows completely straight may irritate them. If so, bend your elbows slightly. Keep this to the minimum, however, or you'll reduce the potential expansion effect on your rib cage.

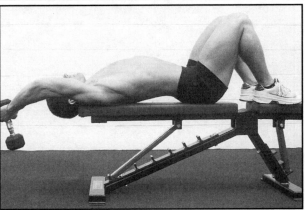

Elbow irritation may come from using more weight than has been recommended, or from not introducing the exercise into your program carefully enough. Elbow irritation may also come from using a straight bar, whereas a parallel grip on a weight plate, or dumbbell(s), may be safe.

The breathing pullover is traditionally done immediately after an exercise that gets you heavily winded, such as the squat, especially when the latter's done for high reps. And it can be done at other times, too.

Go easy at the beginning. The forced and exaggerated breathing may make you feel dizzy unless you work into it progressively over a few weeks. Your chest may get sore, too, if you don't work into the exercise gradually.

CALF RAISE

Main muscles worked

gastrocnemius, soleus

Capsule description

stand with the balls of your feet fixed, then raise and lower your heels

The soleus is underneath the gastrocnemius, so most of the soleus isn't visible, but it still contributes significantly to calf girth. The soleus crosses the ankle joint only, but the gastrocnemius crosses the ankle *and* knee joints. Both muscles plantar flex the foot—namely, point the toes—but the gastrocnemius also assists with flexion of the knee.

The calf raise is often called a *heel raise*. Confusingly, it's also sometimes called a *toe raise* even though the toes don't rise.

There are several types of calf raises: standing using both legs, standing using one leg at a time, seated (usually with both legs working simultaneously), and donkey style (where an assistant sits on the bent-over trainee's hips, for added resistance). Avoid the leg press machine for calf work. This offers nothing that other calf exercises don't, but can be dangerous if your feet slip out of position.

Keeping your knees straight in calf work, or just slightly bent, fully recruits the gastrocnemius *and* the soleus. Bent-knee calf work—especially the seated calf raise—reduces gastrocnemius involvement according to the extent of knee flexion.

The standing two-legged calf raise, and the standing one-legged variation, are the calf exercises used in **Course #1**. Both of these exercises fully involve the gastrocnemius and soleus simultaneously.

Set-up and positioning

In all calf work, place the balls of your feet on a stable block, to enable your heels to descend below the level of the balls of your feet. If the block is free standing—not attached to a calf machine—fix it to a board that has a larger area. This will prevent the block from flipping over. For example, get a 4 x 4 x 20 inch (10 x 10 x 50 cm) piece of wood and nail it to the center of a 1 x 10 x 22 inch (2.5 x 25 x 55 cm) board. Round one of the top two

long edges of the block, for the side where you'll place your feet. As an alternative, at least for the dumbbell one-legged calf raise, use an immovable object such as a step.

Depending on the soles of your shoes and the surface you stand on, your feet may slip out of position during the course of a set of calf raises. If this happens, quickly reposition your feet, but next time try different shoes or a different platform or block (perhaps one with rubber fixed on top of it) to help prevent your feet from slipping. Slipping can, however, be caused by incorrect foot positioning, and excessive range of motion at the bottom of the exercise.

If the full range of motion produces foot problems, cut your range of motion a little. Find the maximum range of motion that's safe for you, and which doesn't lead to your feet slipping off the elevation.

Your calves may be tight at present. The calf stretch described in this book should help you to increase the flexibility of your calves. Then as your flexibility improves you may be able to increase your depth of descent in the calf raise.

Health benefits

As well as the aesthetic benefits of calf development, there are health benefits from regular calf exercise. With age, the return of blood to the heart through the veins decreases in efficiency. This is prominent below the knees, and may lead to varicose veins because of blood pooling, and damage to the venous valves. The venous blood is moved upward through muscle contraction. Inactivity of the calves increases the difficulty of getting the venous blood to the heart. Keep your calves strong and trained.

Standing two-legged calf raise

A machine is needed for this exercise. If one isn't available, stick with the one-legged calf raise.

Compression of the spine may occur in the standing two-legged calf raise if your heels touch the floor *before* the resistance reaches its resting position. Set up the machine so that the resistance rests on a support before your heels touch the floor. Alternatively, use a block high enough so that it's impossible to touch your heels to the floor even at full stretch. If you can't ensure you don't risk compressing your spine, change to the dumbbell one-legged calf raise.

When you get positioned for the first rep of any machine standing calf raise, distribute the weight symmetrically over your back and lower limbs, but don't round your upper back. Put the pads in position on your shoulders, pull your shoulder blades back, bend your knees, and place your feet in position on the foot support. Put the entire balls of your feet on the support, not just your toes. Use a hip-width foot placement rather than a close stance, to help you to keep your balance. Keep your big toes pointing directly forward or slightly outward. None of the stress of the weight should be taken on your shoulders yet. Now, hollow your lower spine slightly, lock your torso, and straighten your knees. Then you'll safely be in the starting position for the first rep, with the resistance bearing down on you.

Don't take the full load of the resistance on your shoulders and then shuffle into position on the foot support or block. Get correctly in position before you take on the resistance.

Hold the calf machine during the exercise, to help keep your balance and maintain a rigid torso. During the course of each set, never allow your back to round, torso to relax, or knees to bend anything more than just slightly, to remove tension from your knees.

Perform the reps smoothly. Go as high as possible at the top of each rep, and contract your calves hard for two to three seconds. Descend under control, reach your safe, bottom position, pause for a second without relaxing, then smoothly push out of it. Never bounce at the bottom of a rep.

Left, correct technique for the standing calf raise—note the proper curvature of the spine. Right, don't round your back while performing any machine standing calf raise.

Some squat machines, with the addition of a block under the balls of the feet, can double as calf machines. Keep your knees straight or slightly bent.

Standing one-legged calf raise

The one-legged calf raise is done while holding a dumbbell on the same side as your working calf, while using a standing calf machine, or with resistance hanging from a belt. With a dumbbell, hold with your free hand something sturdy and stable at about shoulder height, to keep your balance—for example, a bar set at the right height in a power rack.

Put the entire ball of your foot on the elevation, not just your toes. Keep the knee of your working leg straight or just slightly bent during each set, and your big toe pointing directly forward or slightly outward. Bend your non-working limb and keep it out of the way—for example, rest it on the heel of your working limb.

Perform your reps smoothly. Go as high as possible at the top of each rep, and contract your calves hard for two to three seconds. Descend under control, reach your safe, bottom position, pause for a second without relaxing, then smoothly push out of it. Never bounce at the bottom of a rep.

Left, one-legged dumbbell calf raise, holding a horizontal bar for balance. Right, one-legged calf raise using a calf machine.

In all calf work, avoid an exaggerated range of motion at the bottom of the exercise. If you overstretch, you'll lose your foot positioning, and have to re-set, which would mar the set. Descend as far as is comfortable for you without it leading to your feet slipping.

Calf stretching should be done during a flexibility routine, not while strength training.

CHIN-UP AND PULL-UP

Main muscles worked

latissimus dorsi, biceps, brachialis, pectorals, upper back, abdominal wall, forearms

Capsule description

holding a fixed overhead bar, pull yourself up until your chin is above the bar

There's confusion with the names *chin-up* and *pull-up*. In this book, the *chin-up* refers to pulling yourself up on an overhead bar using a supinated grip, and the *pull-up* refers to the same movement but with a pronated grip. Many trainees, however, use the two names interchangeably, regardless of the grip used. Chins involve the biceps much more.

Your ability to pull yourself overhead is influenced by your body fat percentage, and your bodyweight in general. The more body fat you have, and the heavier you are, the harder this exercise will be.

Set-up and positioning

If your overhead bar is adjustable—for example, if you use an Olympic bar on saddles in a power rack—set the height so you can just grab the bar when standing on your toes. The knurling on an Olympic bar will help your grip, especially if you have chalk or rosin on your hands.

If you use a fixed, high, overhead bar, arrange a box or platform of the appropriate height so that you only have to stand on your toes to grab the bar. During the exercise, bend your knees, or keep them straight.

Initially, hold the overhead bar with a supinated grip. Start with a shoulder-width grip, and fine-tune to find the spacing that feels best for your wrists and elbows. A hand spacing a little closer than shoulder-width may work best.

If you can't find a workable supinated grip, try a pronated one. Take a grip two to three inches (five to eight cms) wider on each side than your shoulder-width grip, so that your forearms are vertical at the top position. Regardless of the grip you choose, never use a very wide spacing, and don't pull to the rear of your head. Pulling to the front is safer for your shoulders and neck, and more effective.

A Smith machine has a bar that's adjustable for height, and may be well-knurled. It may be ideal for chin-ups and pull-ups.

Top, chin-up (supinated grip). Middle, pull-up (pronated). Bottom, parallel grip.

Some chinning units provide the option of using a parallel grip. This may be more comfortable than a supinated or a pronated grip on a single bar. The parallel handles may, however, be too close to produce a good training effect.

A possibility for chinning with a parallel grip is to use a power rack. If its uprights are appropriately spaced for you, position a bar on saddles on the front uprights, and another bar across the rear uprights at the same height. Set the height of the bars so that when your elbows are straight, your feet *just* touch the floor.

Performance

Pull until you touch the bar to your collar bones, or lower on your chest. Comparing the same resistance and degree of effort, you'll be able to pull your hands to a lower point on your chest with a supinated or pronated grip than with a parallel one. Fully contract your lats by pulling your shoulder blades *down*.

Your top position will depend, in part, on your grip spacing, forearm and arm lengths, and strength and bodyweight. Don't pull beyond what's comfortable for your shoulders and elbows. Your back should be slightly arched at the top of the exercise. If you have to hump your back in order to finish a rep, the set is finished, you're using too much resistance, or you're not ready, yet, for this exercise.

Pause for a second at the top position, then smoothly lower yourself to an inch short of the bottommost position. Pause for a second at the bottom, then smoothly move into the next ascent. Never drop into the bottom position, or relax and stretch while you're hanging. Keep your eyes looking up slightly, and don't turn your head. Keep your shoulders tight, and your head tilted back, but don't throw your head back.

Inhale as you lower yourself, and exhale during the ascent. Trying to catch your breath during a momentary pause at the bottom position is usually counterproductive unless you can briefly stand or kneel while you breathe.

Other tips

Attach weight securely and comfortably. Use a shoulder harness or a belt designed for hanging weight from, wear a belt and put a dumbbell inside it by having the dumbbell vertical and the belt across the handle, or, use a strong piece of rope or chain to attach a dumbbell or weight plates

securely to a belt. For the latter, the resistance can be hung from the front or the rear of the belt. Try both to find which is most comfortable for you.

Add weight slowly, in small increments. To work from one fixed-weight dumbbell to the next, gradually attach weight to the lighter dumbbell—most easily done by using small magnetic plates. Alternatively, use an adjustable dumbbell, or weight plates only.

Three methods of attaching weight to a belt. These illustrations show use of a lifting belt. Use of a purpose-made weight belt would be better. And at least for small weights, a strong, leather belt normally used for trousers could substitute.

A shoulder harness isn't illustrated, but is the preferred option—for safety, and comfort—if a substantial poundage is to be attached to a suspended body. A substantial poundage attached around the waist or hips to a suspended body may apply an unsafe load on the vertebrae.

The free-weight parallel bar dip—another exercise where the body is suspended—has a greater potential for additional weight to be attached than have the chin-up and the pull-up. But a very strong person may build up to a large weight in the latter two exercises and thus should use a shoulder harness rather than a weight belt.

Spotting

Though not essential, use a spotter if possible. When you grind to a halt short of completing a rep, get a spotter to assist. Enough pressure should be evenly applied to your back. The assistant should push you up in your regular groove, not push you forward and mar the pathway.

CRUNCH

Four forms of the crunch will be described:

> basic crunch
> modified basic crunch
> machine crunch
> reverse crunch

Main muscles worked

rectus abdominis, external and internal abdominal obliques, transversus abdominis, hip flexors, (and the twisting crunch also works the multifidii)

Capsule description

curl your shoulders toward your hips, or your hips toward your shoulders

Exercise for the abdominal muscles is important, and not just for aesthetic reasons. Strong, well-developed abdominals help to keep the lower back strong and resistant to injury because they help to stabilize the spine during many exercises.

Crunches come in two basic types: The basic crunch curls the shoulders toward the hips, and the reverse crunch curls the hips toward the chest. Each works both functions of the rectus abdominis and transversus abdominis—compression of the abdomen, and flexion of the trunk—but only two of the functions of the obliques: compression of the abdomen, and flexion of the trunk. A third function of the obliques—trunk rotation—isn't worked by most crunches. The twisting crunch employs rotation.

The rectus abdominis ("six-pack") is one long, flat, continuous muscle that runs from the lower ribs to the groin. While it's not possible to isolate the upper or lower abdominals, the two sections may respond differently to flexion exercises that require the shoulders to move toward the hips, than to flexion exercises that require the hips to move toward the shoulders.

Trainees commonly get poor results from crunches for two main reasons: many perform excessive reps with little or no added resistance, and most use incorrect technique regardless of their rep count. With correct technique, moderate reps, and progressive resistance, good results will come. But whether you'll see your abdominal development will depend on how much fat you have covering your midsection.

Preparatory movement

Before every rep of any crunch, tilt your hips so that your lumbar vertebrae are pushed into the floor or mat.

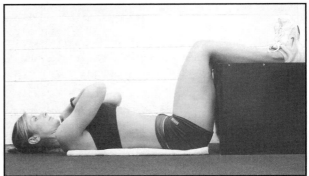

Why sit-ups are dangerous

Especially in days gone by, school students and youngsters elsewhere were urged by instructors to perform quick-fire sit-ups with their knees *straight*, and hands interlocked behind their heads or necks. That technique can be harmful even for youngsters, and is potentially harmful for most adults. Avoid it.

Crunches are safe, relative to sit-ups, because the knees are bent, the hips are flexed, and the lower back is rounded to the *rear*. As a result, the abdominal muscles pull you up and forward, and the hip flexors help as synergists (not prime movers) to keep the pelvis stabilized at the crucial moment the crunch is initiated by the rectus abdominis muscles.

But in sit-ups with straight knees, the hip flexors are the prime movers as they first pull the lower spine into a more arched position (curved to the *front*), and *then* they pull the torso up and forward. It's this initial pull on the lumbar arch that feels uncomfortable, and commonly creates problems.

Perform crunches, not sit-ups with straight knees.

Basic crunch

Lie on a mat next to a bench. Bend your knees at a right angle and rest your calves on the bench. Don't cross your legs. Get an assistant to hold your legs on the bench, use a purpose-built bench with a leg restraint, or brace your feet in some way so that your legs stay fixed to the bench. Cross your hands and rest them on your chest or shoulders. Before each rep, tilt your pelvis so that while your coccyx and sacrum come off the floor a little (that is, your buttocks rise slightly), your lumbar vertebrae are pushed into the floor. Smoothly curl your torso off the floor until your forearms touch your thighs. Pause for a second at the top position, and contract your abdominals hard. Then take about three seconds to smoothly unfurl onto the floor. Maintain the pelvic tilt during the ascent and descent. Once your shoulders are on the floor, pause for a second, again push your lumbar vertebrae into the floor (that is, tilt your pelvis), and repeat.

Don't hold your breath. Exhale fully before the lifting phase, and inhale during the descent.

Keep your head and neck in one position during each rep, with your chin slightly off your chest.

A common mistake is putting the hands behind the head. This leads to pulling on the head, causing neck irritation. When you require resistance, hold a dumbbell across your chest, with the handle parallel with your shoulders. You could hold small plates on your chest, but large plates will obstruct the proper movement. Once you've progressed beyond using small plates, move to a dumbbell. Be consistent with where you place the dumbbell on your mid to upper chest, so that you apply resistance in the same way each time. If you vary the position of the dumbbell, you'll change the perceived weight of the resistance.

Loading and unloading the resistance can be a problem—because asymmetrical movement is involved in taking a dumbbell from the floor at one side, for example. Have an assistant put the dumbbell directly on your chest, and remove it for you at the end of the set.

Hip flexors, and ab work

The hip flexors are involved in most forms of abdominal work, including crunches. (The iliopsoas hip flexors—iliacus, psoas major, and psoas minor—are located deep in the pelvis, and are hidden from view. The other major hip flexor, the rectus femoris, is visible—it's part of the quadriceps.) The degree of involvement of the hip flexors depends on the technique used. Abdominal work with straight knees may employ the hip flexors to a greater extent than the abs, and should be avoided. By keeping the knees bent, the involvement of the hip flexors is reduced, and the relative involvement of the abs is increased. Substantial hip flexor involvement can produce lower-back problems for many trainees—typically those whose lower backs aren't strong enough, and who lack sufficient flexibility. Generally, the greater the hip flexor involvement in abdominal work, the greater the possibility of lower-back irritation.

If you've had any back problems, use the *modified* basic crunch for a few months before you consider progressing to the full-range basic crunch. The modified crunch has a reduced range of motion relative to the basic crunch, and involves the hip flexors to a lesser extent. This reduced hip flexor involvement means reduced stress on the lower back. In the meantime, get checked out by a chiropractor, strengthen your abs with the modified basic crunch, strengthen your lower back with back extensions, and work on the flexibility routine.

The hip flexor involvement in the basic crunch is desirable *provided* the exercise can be done safely. The hip flexors need to be strengthened, too, once the lower back and abs have been sufficiently strengthened. What's required is balanced strength across the three areas.

Modified basic crunch

Adopt the same set-up as for the basic crunch, although it may not be necessary to have your calves held against the bench. The modified crunch is a short-range exercise. Only about half your spine should come off the floor. Your lumbar vertebrae must retain contact with the floor throughout each rep.

Use a slow ascent and forcible crunch of your abdominal muscles. Hold the top position for a second. Slowly lower your upper back to the floor. Move smoothly at all times.

Don't hold your breath. Exhale fully before the lifting phase, and inhale during the descent.

Machine crunch

Follow the manufacturer's guidelines for the set-up.

Smoothly flex the upper half of your spine. Crunch your torso forward, hold the intense contraction for a second, then smoothly return to the starting position. Pause for a second, then smoothly begin the next rep.

Don't hold your breath. Exhale fully before the flexion phase, and inhale during the extension.

Compare the effect from the machine on your abdominals with that from the non-machine crunches. The latter may be better, because many crunch machines aren't well designed.

The crunch machine shown at the top has the resistance arms above the chest. The other has a resistance pad applied against the chest.

Reverse crunch

Lie on your back on a horizontal bench. Hold the bench behind your head. With straight knees, lift your legs so that they are perpendicular to the bench. Keep your feet directly above your hips, and bend your knees so that they are above your lower chest. Tilt your pelvis so that while your coccyx and sacrum come off the bench a little, your lumbar vertebrae are pushed into the bench. Initiate every rep in this manner. Then roll your lower back off the bench. Hold the top position for a second, then slowly return to the starting position. Pause for a second, tilt your pelvis again, and smoothly move into the next rep.

This is a short-range movement. Maintain the pelvic tilt throughout each rep. At no point should you arch or hollow your lower spine.

Don't hold your breath. Exhale fully before the concentric or lifting phase, and inhale during the descent or eccentric phase.

Performing the reverse crunch on a horizontal bench with your feet above your hips and knees bent above your lower chest, provides low resistance. To increase the resistance, straighten your knees but keep your feet above your hips. To further increase the resistance, keep your thighs perpendicular to the bench, and knees bent so that your feet are in front of your hips. Progress until you can perform your target reps with your knees bent at a right angle and thighs vertical. For increased resistance thereafter, perform the reverse crunch on an incline bench, with your head higher than your hips in the starting position.

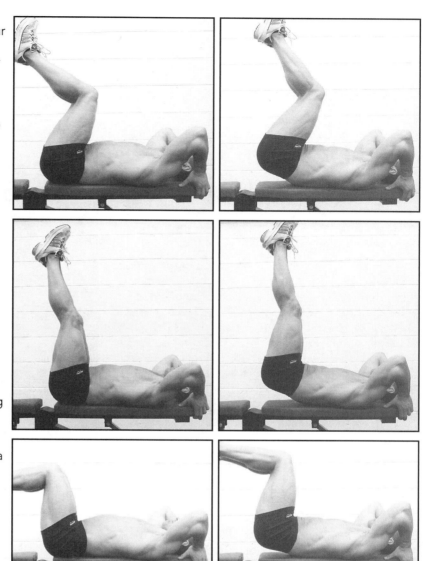

The topmost photographs show the least demanding of these three forms of the reverse crunch. If required, the resistance can be further reduced by bringing the knees closer to the chest.

The bottommost photographs show the most demanding of these three forms of the reverse crunch. To make it even more taxing, perform the reverse crunch on an inclined bench, with your head above your hips in the starting position—the photograph on the left page shows the top position. Start with little inclination, and increase the degree of slope gradually.

Remember to tilt your pelvis so that your lower spine (other than your coccyx and sacrum) is flattened against the bench prior to each rep—for safety, and to focus the stress on your abs.

In all variations of the reverse crunch, don't jam your head onto the bench, because that could cause neck injury. Maintain a relaxed neck, and keep the strain of the exercise on your abdominals.

CURL

Main muscles worked

biceps, brachialis, brachioradialis, forearms

Capsule description

standing or seated, with your arms and forearms hanging straight, lift the weight through bending at your elbows

The curl can be done with dumbbells or a barbell, standing or seated. If done seated, use dumbbells in order to extend your forearms fully. There are also cable and machine variations of the curl.

The biceps flex the elbows *and* supinate the hands and forearms. To supinate your hands fully, rotate them from a palms-down to a palms-up position. You can't do this with a barbell. The biceps isn't the only elbow flexor. There are the brachialis (beneath the biceps) and the brachioradialis (from just above the elbow, to the wrist), too, which are also worked by the curl. The latter two muscles flex the elbow only, they don't supinate the hand.

To fully involve all of your arm flexors, use a curl that requires full supination of your forearms.

While permitting supination and a full range of motion even while seated, the dumbbell curl produces another advantage over the barbell curl—the ability for the wrists and elbows to adopt the most comfortable positioning.

In all curls, keep your wrists and hands in a straight line—the neutral position. If you don't maintain the neutral position, you may develop wrist and elbow problems.

The correct, straight, or neutral position of hands and wrists (top), and the incorrect position (above).

Spotting

Technique deterioration is shown through leaning back (unless you use back support) and bringing the elbows too far forward. As soon as your torso goes back even a whisker beyond the vertical, your spotter should urge you to straighten up. If you perform another rep, a little assistance may be needed if you're to complete the rep in correct technique. Assistance should be applied with two hands, in a symmetrical way. Just enough help should be given to keep your torso and arms vertical.

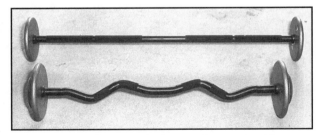

Comparison of a straight bar and an ez-curl bar. The ez-curl bar may be more comfortable to use for the curl than a straight bar, but at the price of reduced biceps involvement because it decreases the supination of the forearms.

Seated dumbbell curl

Sit at the end of a bench, knees together, and feet on the floor. Hold a dumbbell in each hand, with straight elbows, hands parallel with each other, an upright torso, and your shoulders retracted.

Curl the dumbbells, don't swing them—move smoothly. As the dumbbells ascend, supinate your hands as much as possible—rotate your thumbs outward. On the descent, pronate your hands so that, in the starting position, they are parallel with each other once again.

Start with your elbows at your sides so that your arms are vertical when viewed from the side and from the front. As you curl, your elbows may come forward only slightly. At the top position, your hands should be short of where they would be to make your forearms perfectly vertical. Your hands may come to shoulder height, but no higher.

Pause for a second in the top position. Contract your biceps hard as you fully supinate your wrists. It's not possible to rest at the top of a properly performed curl. Lower the resistance under control, pause for a second at the bottom position, then smoothly perform the next rep. Exhale during the ascent, and inhale during the descent.

Incline dumbbell curl

Perform the dumbbell curl with your hips, back, and shoulders against an incline bench set at about 45 degrees. For comfort, your head doesn't have to rest against the bench. To make it easy to pick up the dumbbells from the floor, use the lowest seat setting, if it's adjustable. And because of the incline bench, your arms may not be perfectly vertical. Otherwise, the technique is the same as for the *Seated dumbbell curl*.

Barbell curl

Stand with your feet about hip-width apart. Keep your knees slightly unlocked, and your buttocks tensed, to help support your spine. Use a supinated (palms-up) grip on the barbell, with hands spaced a little wider than hip-width. Fine-tune this to find the hand spacing that's most comfortable for your wrists and elbows. Other than there being no wrist rotation in the barbell curl, the rest of the technique is the same as for the *Seated dumbbell curl*.

If the straight bar irritates your elbows or wrists, try a closer or wider grip. If that doesn't correct the problem, use dumbbells with as much supination of your forearms as is comfortable. Use of an ez-curl bar is an inferior option. The bends or cambers in an ez-curl bar decrease forearm supination, which in turn decreases biceps contraction.

Hammer curl

Different wrist positions produce different effects on the elbow flexors, and apply stress differently to the elbow joints. An option is to keep your thumbs up all the time—the *hammer curl*. If you've had wrist, elbow or shoulder problems, the hammer curl may be the variation that feels the most comfortable. The hammer curl may be performed standing (illustrated), seated at the end of a horizontal bench, or seated on an incline bench.

But because there's so little supination of the forearms in the hammer curl, there's a price to pay—greatly reduced biceps involvement.

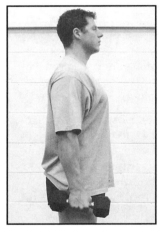

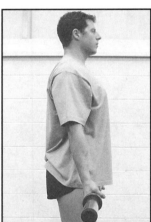

Correct starting and finishing positions.

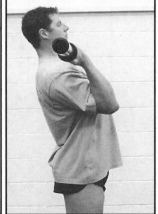

Incorrect finishing positions.

DEADLIFT

The *basic*, or *conventional*, or *regular*, or *bent-legged* deadlift (with a *straight* bar), is what's usually meant by *the deadlift*. But a specification of *basic*, *conventional*, *regular* or *bent-legged* isn't normally used. This can lead to confusion because there are several forms of deadlifting: deadlift (conventional style), parallel-grip deadlift, partial deadlift, stiff-legged deadlift, and sumo deadlift.

Properly done, variations of the deadlift are among the most effective bodybuilding exercises. But use poor technique, abuse low reps, overtrain, or try to lift weights that are too heavy for you, and you'll hurt yourself with any form of the deadlift.

Just two forms of the deadlift are described here, because only these variations are employed in **Course #1**: parallel-grip deadlift
            partial deadlift

See page 24 for the reasons why the parallel-grip deadlift is employed in **Course #1** *as a linchpin exercise rather than the conventional deadlift.*

If you've had a serious back injury, don't deadlift without the clearance of a chiropractor. If you've had any minor back injuries, still get a chiropractor's clearance.

Critical note for all deadlifts

The greater the extent of the forward lean, the greater the risk to the back because of the increased chance of losing the slightly concave lower spine that's essential for safe deadlifting. To try to minimize the risk from deadlifting, keep your maximum forward lean to about 45 degrees from an imaginary vertical line. There has to be forward lean in order to heavily involve the back musculature, but excessive forward lean must be avoided. A slightly concave lower spine must be maintained.

To accurately determine your back positioning during any type of deadlift, get an assistant to watch you from the side (while crouched, to view you from about your hip height), and provide you with instant feedback. You can't see what's happening to your back in the reflection in a mirror in front of you, and you shouldn't watch yourself in a side-on mirror while you exercise.

"Flat back" confusion

The spine is curved when seen from the side. This curvature is the natural, strong structure for absorbing and distributing stress efficiently. When the curves are lost, the strong, load-bearing capability is diminished.

"Keep a flat back" is a common admonition when lifting a weight, and one that I've used in my earlier writing. It's not, however, an accurate one. What it really means, is, "Don't round your lower back." Although it may look like the lower back is flat at the bottom of a correctly performed deadlift or squat, as examples, this is an illusion. When contracted, the spinal erectors, if sufficiently developed, may fill the required slight hollow in the lower spine's profile at those bottom positions, giving an impression that the lower back is flat, but the actual lower *spine* should be slightly concave, or hollow.

It's the strong contraction of the lumbar musculature that produces the extended, concave lower spine, to create a bracing effect. The strong contraction of the muscles on both sides of the spine not only prevents the forward rounding of the back, but helps prevent sideways, asymmetrical bending as well.

If the lower *spine* is truly flat, the upper back will be rounded, which is a dangerous position when lifting a challenging weight (or even a light one in many cases). A spine that's intentionally straightened while under heavy load bearing is a weakened one that's exposed to an increased risk of injury. And a spine that's naturally straight suggests pathology.

When lifting a weight, inside or outside of the gym, keep your shoulders retracted, hips pushed back (extended), and lower spine slightly hollow. There are exceptions, however. For example, during the back extension the back *should* round, and during crunches the lower spine shouldn't be hollow—keep it flat against the floor.

Parallel-grip deadlift

Main muscles worked

spinal erectors, multifidii, buttocks, quadriceps, thigh adductors, hamstrings, latissimus dorsi, upper back, forearms

Capsule description

with knees well bent, and a slightly hollow lower spine, lift the resistance from the floor

Properly done, the parallel-grip deadlift is one of the most effective exercises—a big, multi-joint exercise that works most of the musculature in the body, namely the thighs, buttocks, and back. There are a number of pieces of equipment used for performing parallel-grip deadlifts, primarily the trap bar, the shrug bar, and dumbbells. The dumbbells are the trickiest to use—they get in the way of the lower limbs, constrain stance width and flare more than the one-piece bars, may prohibit ideal foot positioning, and thus hamper technique. Furthermore, many gyms don't have dumbbells heavy enough for trainees other than beginners. Consequently, it's the technique of deadlifting with a one-piece, parallel-grip bar that's described in this section.

Before you can parallel-grip deadlift with correct technique, you need to be flexible enough to adopt the necessary positioning. You especially need flexible calves, hamstrings, thigh adductors, and buttocks.

With the conventional deadlift, the problem of getting a straight bar around the knees is what produces the increased forward lean and reduced knee flexion compared with the parallel-grip deadlift. With the latter, you're inside the bar, as against behind it with the straight-bar deadlift. This is what permits the reduced forward lean and increased knee flexion in the parallel-grip deadlift, and potentially makes it a safer exercise.

With the parallel-grip deadlift you can use more knee flexion than in the regular deadlift, hand spacing is determined by the bar's gripping sites (about 22 to 24 inches apart, or 56 to 61 centimeters, depending on the manufacturer), and the bar doesn't drag against your thighs. The pathway of an imaginary straight line joining the ends of the parallel-grip bar can run through you, rather than in front of you like with a straight bar.

Don't perform parallel-grip deadlift reps continuously, touch-and-go, or, worse of all, bounce-and-go. Set the bar down after each rep. Each rep starts and finishes at the bottom.

A "dead lift" means to lift a "dead" weight—one that's stationary. Conventional squats and bench presses, for example, don't have this pause at the bottom—they aren't "dead" weight exercises. (Some trainees do, however, train the squat and the bench press from a dead stop at the bottom, but that's for specialist purposes, and not how they are done in **Course #1**.)

Don't parallel-grip deadlift in an exaggeratedly upright manner, to try to increase stress on your quads. A natural spread of work between your thighs and back produces the right balance to give you your biggest strength potential.

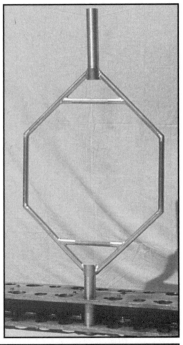

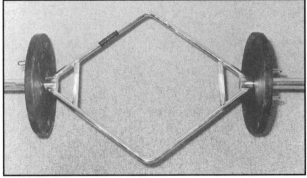

Two examples of parallel-grip bars: the preferred shrug bar (top), and the trap bar.

Surface to deadlift on

Barbell plates roll easily on a smooth floor or platform. Always check that your feet are in the right position relative to the bar before each rep, and adjust them (or the bar) if need be.

The rolling of the plates can be minimized if you deadlift on some hard-wearing, non-slip carpet or rubber fixed to a wooden surface, because of the give in the carpet or rubber. A piece of plywood large enough to accommodate you and your bar, with a carpet or rubber surface, would serve you well— a piece of about 84 x 36 x 1 inch (210 x 90 x 2.5 centimeters) would suffice.

Stance

As a starting point, use a hip-width heel spacing, with your toes turned out about 20 degrees on each side. Fine-tune this to suit you—a little wider, or a little closer. (The wider your stance, the more your toes should be flared, and vice versa.) Your legs must fit inside your hands when your hands are on the handles, but without your knees moving inward. Your knees must be in the same plane as your feet. If your feet are too wide, your knees will travel inward to make room for your hands and forearms during the lower part of each rep.

If you can't use this stance safely, the parallel-grip deadlift isn't suited to you. The more roomy inside area of the shrug bar, compared with the trap bar, may provide greater stance options. This is why the shrug bar is preferred to the trap bar.

With the spacing of your heels determined, place your feet inside the bar in the best position for you. As a starting point, place your feet so that the center of the ends of the bar runs through the bony prominence in the center of the outside of each of your ankles, as you stand with your knees straight.

Although this foot positioning will suit some people, for others it may not be ideal. Try it with a light weight, and see. Then, for example, move your feet back an inch, and see how that works. And try an inch forward of the original positioning, too.

Optimal foot positioning is affected by your body structure, and degree of knee flexion. You may need several workouts of practice, and trial and error, before you settle on the optimum foot positioning for you.

If you're positioned too far to the rear, you'll probably be bent forward too much and the bar may swing as you lift it off the floor. If you're positioned too far to the front, the bar will probably

The parallel-grip deadlift. At the bottom position, the inward curvature of the model's lower spine is filled with contracted erector spinae muscle, presenting the appearance of a flat back. The trap bar is tipping here, but should be horizontal.

Note the natural balance between forward lean and knee bend that evenly spreads the stress over the entire lifting structure, for maximum strength potential. There's no exaggerated upright torso and exaggerated knee bend, or exaggerated forward bend and minimized knee bend. But individual body structure will influence the degree of forward bend and knee bend.

also swing as you lift it off the floor. There should be no swinging of the bar.

Once you know the foot positioning that works best for you, use a reference point so that you can adopt the right set-up each time.

You could use ankle position relative to an imaginary line running through the ends of the bar, for example. Or, you could use the position of the front rim of your shoes relative to the front of the rhombus. Your eyes must, however, view from the same point each time. For example, as you stand upright, cast your eyes down and perhaps the front rim of your shoes is directly below the inside edge of the front of the rhombus. Perhaps it's an inch inside.

Check that your stance relative to the bar is correct before every rep. It's possible that when you set the bar down after completing a rep, it's a little out of position. Reposition the bar, or adjust your feet to compensate.

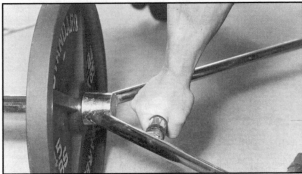

A piece of garden hose of the right size, and appropriately positioned, permits hand centering on a parallel-grip bar's handle without having to look down to check. See text. The legs were kept out of the photos, so as not to obstruct viewing.

Grip

Use a parallel-grip bar with knurled handles.

If your hands are off center on the handles, the parallel-grip bar will tip. If only one hand is off center, dangerous rotational stress may result. Keep both hands correctly centered, and the bar parallel with the floor.

Here's how to center your hands on the handles without having to look down and lose the tensed torso and correct get-set position: Slice open two small pieces of garden hose, and slip one over each handle, flush against the front bar. Cut the length so that when you feel your hand touching the edge of the hose, your hand is centered. Slip the lengths in position prior to when you parallel-grip deadlift.

When you place the handles in your hands, place them against the part of your palm right at the base of your fingers. If you place the handles in the center of your palms, gravity will pull the handles towards the base of your fingers anyway during the course of the set, but trap a fold of skin there, which is uncomfortable and can increase callus formation. Best to start the exercise with the bar in the right place. The wrong hand position also

increases the range of motion a little, until gravity puts the bar in its proper position.

Start

With your feet and the bar already in the correct positions, stand and get ready for the first rep.

Here's the torso set you need to fight to maintain throughout the parallel-grip deadlift: While standing, take your final big breath, keep a high chest, tense your upper-back muscles, and rotate your shoulders back into a military posture. This will tend to push your arms out away from your body, as your lats will be hard. Your lower spine will be slightly hollow, or concave.

Start the descent with a synchronized bending of your knees *and* a natural forward lean of your torso. Sit down *and* back, and push your hips to the rear. Always maintain a slightly hollow lower spine, and keep your shoulder blades retracted.

As you descend, keep your bodyweight primarily over your heels, but don't rock back and lose your balance. Descend until your hands touch the handles. Center your hands as explained earlier—without having to look down.

At the bottom position, your knees should be bent substantially, hips much lower than your shoulders, neck neutral (neither extended nor flexed) or just slightly extended, and your bodyweight felt mostly through your heels.

Ascent

The first part of the ascent is to shrug your shoulders vertically against the bar. Although you won't lift the bar unless it's light, this shrug helps to lock your back into the right (extended) position for the pull. Stick your chest out, too. Then squeeze the bar off the floor through simultaneously pushing with your thighs—mostly through your heels—*and* pulling with your back.

Push through both your feet with equal force. If you favor one limb you'll produce a dangerous corkscrew-like motion. Think of pushing your feet through the floor. Keep your shoulders pulled back, scapulae retracted, and chest pushed up and out.

Make the start of the ascent smooth and slow. Don't yank at the bar. Yanking leads to bending your elbows, moving you forward, raising your hips too quickly, and increasing stress on your back.

Your hips mustn't rise faster than your shoulders, because that would increase your degree of

Common errors: Left, hips are too high for the starting position, producing excessive forward lean, and loss of the correct back set. Right, following a correct start (not illustrated here) the hips have moved too fast, producing loss of back set, and rounding of the back.

forward lean. At the start of the ascent, your back must maintain the same angle with the floor. Your back angle decreases later in the ascent, from approximately after the bar clears your knees.

The parallel-grip deadlift is done by the thighs and back *together*. If you start the ascent only with your thighs, your knees will straighten too quickly, you'll lean forward more, and your back will then bear the brunt of the load. But if you start the ascent with little thigh involvement you won't get far unless it's a light weight for you.

Once the bar is off the floor and moving, try to accelerate its speed. Again, push through both your feet with equal force. Think of pushing your feet through the floor, mostly through your heels. And keep your shoulders pulled back and chest pushed up and out—that should keep your back slightly hollow throughout. *Never* round your back.

Look forward, which means that there will be some neck extension, or look slightly down, which means that your neck will be in a more neutral position.

Over the final few inches of the ascent, fight to keep your shoulders pulled back, and chest pushed up and out. If your shoulders slump, your back will round, stress on your spine and its musculature will increase greatly, and you'll set yourself up for a serious injury. Part of the reason why the shrug should be included in your training program at least some of the time is to help you to develop the strength required to keep your shoulders pulled back even under stress.

Remain *vertical* at the top of the lift. If you lean back at the top, that would cause dangerous compression of your intervertebral discs.

As you stand, keep your scapulae retracted, lower spine slightly hollow, weight felt mostly through your heels, and your shoulders, hips, and ankles lined up. Pause for a second, then start the descent.

Descent with the bar

Simultaneously bend at your hips *and* your knees during the descent. And guide the bar, don't just lower it. Your hands should follow a line along the center of your thighbones and, further down, along the center of the sides of your calves.

When your hands are at knee height, they should also be in line with your knees. If your hands get behind that line, you risk being too upright. Your hands may, however, be a little forward of that line.

Keep your shoulder blades retracted, and chest pushed up and out, as you lower the bar deliberately and symmetrically. Sit down *and* back—push your hips to the rear. Always maintain a slightly hollow lower spine.

To keep correct control over the bar, take about three seconds for the descent. Gently set the bar on the floor or platform. Never drop the bar or bounce it. Be in control of it at all times.

Rest pauses

For the parallel-grip deadlift, if you pause between reps as you stand while holding the bar, your grip will fail before you've adequately worked your major muscular structures. And your freedom to breathe deeply will be compromised. Instead, set the bar on the floor and stand between reps while you take your deep breaths.

Alternatively, pause while the weight is on the floor, your hands still on the bar but relaxed, and your knees straight; then take your deep breaths, take your final deep breath and immediately squat down and get into position to perform the next rep with the correct torso set, then immediately do the rep, and so on. You may find the effect on your chest from the deep breathing to be more pronounced with the latter method.

Try both options. You may find the second alternative to be more suited to the early reps in a hard 20-rep set, and the first alternative to be more suited to the harder reps at the end of the set.

Other special breathing requirements for 20-rep parallel-grip deadlifts are covered elsewhere in this book, including on page 57.

Other tips

While experimenting to find your optimum stance, and while using a very light weight, stand on some card when you parallel-grip deadlift. When you think you've found your stance, draw around your feet with a marker. Next session, you'll know where you were positioned last time. When you settle on a stance that works best for you, mark it on cardboard and refer to it when required.

For work sets once the weight becomes demanding, use chalk or rosin on your hands to improve your grip on the bar.

Always parallel-grip deadlift with collars on the bar. This is critical for keeping the plates in position, and the bar balanced.

Never turn your head while you lift or lower the bar, or otherwise the bar will tip somewhat, your lifting groove will be marred, and you could hurt yourself.

If you can't complete a rep without your shoulders slumping, dump the weight. End the set of your own volition before you get hurt.

Never drop the weight, even if you have to dump it because you feel your back about to start rounding. Protecting the equipment and floor is only part of the reason for lowering the bar with control. A bar slamming on the floor or platform can injure your back, shoulders, elbows, or wrists. Lowering the weight too quickly can also lead to rounding the back and losing the important slightly arched lower spine.

Once you're training hard, never parallel-grip deadlift to failure. Keep the "do or die" rep in you.

Don't parallel-grip deadlift while your lower back is still sore from an earlier workout, or heavy manual labor. Rest a day or two longer, until the soreness has gone away.

As seen from the side view, get feedback from an assistant, or record yourself with a video camera. Discover your actual hip, shoulder and head positions. The technique you think you use may not be what you actually use.

Once you've mastered parallel-grip deadlifting technique, don't become overconfident. Just a slight slip of concentration can lead to errors.

Deadlifts can cause callus buildup on your hands. If this is excessive, your skin may become vulnerable

This home-gym trainee is using plates of smaller diameter than the usual 20-kilo or 45-pound ones. Such plates lead to an exaggerated range of motion that's unsafe for many bodybuilders. By using a pair of platforms—for example, as illustrated—the range of motion can be reduced as required.

to cracks and tears. Both may temporarily restrict your training. Avoid excessive build-up of calluses. Once a week, after you've showered or bathed, use a pumice stone or callus file and gently rub the calluses on your hands. Don't cut the calluses with a blade or scissors. Keep the calluses under control so that they don't cause loss of elasticity on the skin under and around them. To help maintain the elasticity of the skin of your palms and fingers, consume enough essential fatty acids.

Range of motion

The range of motion produced from using 45-pound or 20-kilo plates on the parallel-grip bar is appropriate for many bodybuilders. (Lightweight plates with the diameter of a 45-pound or 20-kilo plate are available, for novices.) But if the correct back positioning can't be maintained at the bottom of the parallel-grip deadlift, the range of motion may need to be reduced by elevating the bar a little—put some matting or wood under the plates.

But with increased flexibility, and work on improving technique, the correct back positioning may be possible at the initial range of motion.

Some parallel-grip deadlift bars have elevated handles (not illustrated), which reduce the range of deadlifting motion when compared with bars with regular handles, provided that both types of bars are loaded with the same diameter plates.

The elevated handles may suit you if you can't safely use the full range of motion with 45-pound or 20-kilo plates on a regular parallel-grip bar.

If, however, you can safely use the full range of motion but only have access to a bar with raised handles, elevate yourself on a sturdy, non-slip surface the same height as the elevation of the handles, or use smaller-diameter plates.

The parallel-grip deadlift can be modified to increase thigh involvement beyond what's yielded from using 45-pound or 20-kilo plates on a bar with regular handles. Perform it from a raised surface, to increase the range of motion. The two critical provisos are that your lower spine can be kept slightly hollow during this increased range of motion, and you have no knee limitations. If you can satisfy these provisos, rejoice. The increased range of motion may make the parallel-grip deadlift even more effective for you.

To try a raised surface, start with no more than one inch. If, after a few weeks, all is well—correct technique maintained, with no knee or back problems—perhaps try a further half inch, and so on, up to a maximum of two to three inches (five to eight centimeters).

Two 15-kilo plates, smooth sides up, can be placed side-by-side under a parallel-grip bar, to produce a raised, stable surface from which to deadlift for increased quadriceps involvement provided that the correct back set is maintained, and the increased range of motion is safe for the trainee.

Spotting

Spotting isn't required in the parallel-grip deadlift—*never* perform assisted or forced reps in this exercise, or negative-only reps. An alert and knowledgeable assistant can, however, critique your technique, and help keep it correct.

Partial deadlift

Main muscles worked

spinal erectors, multifidii, buttocks, hamstrings, latissimus dorsi, upper back, forearms

Capsule description

with a slightly hollow lower spine, straight elbows, and slightly bent knees, lift a bar from knee height

The partial deadlift described here is a variation of what's commonly called a *stiff-legged deadlift*. Importantly, the variation is done with a *reduced* range of motion.

The partial deadlift is often used as a substitute for the conventional deadlift for trainees who have safety concerns for their backs due to the greater range of motion of the regular deadlift. Substantial back, buttock, hamstring, and grip involvement remain, but quadriceps involvement is minimized.

Performance

In a power rack find the pin setting that puts the bar three to four inches (eight to ten centimeters) below the bottom of your kneecaps. That's the bottom position. Alternatively, set a loaded bar on boxes at the height so that the bar's starting position is the same as in the rack set-up.

Stand with your feet under the bar, heels about hip-width apart, feet parallel with each other or flared a little, and bar touching your *vertical* shins. Take a shoulder-width or slightly wider overhand grip. For reasons explained in the section on the parallel-grip deadlift, when you place the bar in your hands, place it against the part of your palm right at the base of your fingers, not in the center of your palms.

For just the first rep, bend your knees more than slightly, to help ensure correct back positioning. Take a deep breath, pull your shoulders back, hollow your lower spine slightly and, with straight

elbows, shrug against the bar and pull your shoulders back, and push your chest up and out. The bar won't move unless the weight is light, but the shrug will lock your lower spine into the required, slightly hollow position. Now, while looking forward or just slight downward, *simultaneously* pull with your back *and* straighten your knees, to move the bar.

During subsequent reps, bend your knees only slightly. Your knees should straighten as you complete the lift, and bend slightly again during the next descent. Keep your shoulder blades retracted, and chest pushed up and out. During the descent, push your hips rearward, to help keep your lower spine in the correct hollow position. The bar should brush your knees or thighs. Don't lean back at the top. Stand straight, pause for a second, keep your scapulae retracted and lower spine hollow (without exaggeration), then lower the bar to the pins through bending your knees slightly and simultaneously leaning forward.

Don't rest the bar on the pins or boxes. Instead, pause for a second just above the pins. Maintain a locked, hollow lower spine, with your shoulders pulled back and chest pushed up and out. Smoothly move into the next rep.

Exhale during the ascent, or at the top. Then inhale and make the descent.

Lift and lower symmetrically, and don't turn your head. Furthermore, don't let your shoulders round. If your shoulders start to slump, and you can't pull them back, dump the bar instantly but with control.

A lower position for the bottom of the partial deadlift, illustrated outside of a power rack. This trainee—because of his flexibility, strength, and technique—can maintain the correct back set even at this degree of forward lean, and range of motion. But most trainees can't, and thus for safety should use a range of motion like that shown on the previous page. Individual leverages—torso and limb lengths, and their relative proportions—affect performance in deadlift variations, and other exercises. Some trainees are better constructed to perform a given exercise than are others.

This trainee shows excessive neck extension. A more neutral position is recommended.

The partial deadlift can be done with a straight bar, or a parallel-grip bar such as a shrug bar. With a parallel-grip bar, it has to be done from boxes, because the bar isn't long enough for use inside a power rack unless the bar has elongated ends.

Even with chalk or rosin on your hands, and a well-knurled straight bar, you may eventually be forced to use a reverse grip. But using a mixed grip results in a tendency to twist somewhat during the deadlift, and produce an asymmetrical motion, and an increased risk of injury. To balance out this rotational effect, and reduce injury potential, alternate from set to set which way around you have the mixed grip. Even if you find one way around to be more favorable than the other, still work it the other way around, too.

To offset the rotational effect, experiment with having your supinated hand one to two inches (two to five centimeters) nearer the center of the bar than your pronated hand.

Danger

Avoid the full-range stiff-legged deadlift.

The further the torso is leaned forward, the more difficult it is to maintain the proper set position of the back where the lower spine is slightly hollow. The full-range stiff-legged deadlift takes the forward lean to an extreme, where the lower spine rounds. This massively increases the stress on the various structures of the back, and greatly increases the risk of injury. Back rounding is valuable for working the spinal musculature, but it should take place in back extensions, not in any form of the deadlift, whether with bent knees or straight knees.

The full-range stiff-legged deadlift while standing on the floor (top), and the version while standing on a box. The former is the most common form of the full-range stiff-legged deadlift, but it's sometimes done on an elevated surface for an even greater range of motion. For safety, both should be avoided. Notice the back rounding, and the severe loss of back set.

PARALLEL BAR DIP

Main muscles worked

pectorals, triceps, deltoids, latissimus dorsi

Capsule description

while on parallel bars, lower and raise yourself through bending at your elbows

Most bodybuilders can dip safely provided they use correct, controlled technique. If you've had shoulder problems in the past, and the dip bothers you no matter how careful you are, you may still be able to use the machine version safely.

Men who have the most difficulty with dips are frequently heavy. Other factors that lead to difficulty with dips are rounded shoulders, and shortened pectoral muscles. If you're tight in those areas, work for a few weeks on gradually increasing your shoulder and pectoral flexibility before you start dipping.

Female beginners usually have difficulty with the dip, but can prosper on the machine version. The orthodox dip has bodyweight as the minimum resistance; but with the machine dip, resistance starts from almost nothing.

Set-up

If there are multiple pairs of parallel bars, or an adjustable pair, try various width positions. About 22 inches or 56 centimeters between the centers of the bars is a good starting point for most men. Women and slender or small men will be more comfortable with closer bars. Big men may prefer wider bars. Try v-shaped bars to find the optimum hand spacing for you. Face the part of the unit where the v-shaped bars come *together*. Another option is to use a power rack. If its uprights are suitably spaced, position a bar on saddles on the front uprights, and another on the rear uprights. Set the height of the bars at what's ideal for you.

Some v-shaped bars have thick handles, which enable the load to be spread over a bigger area of the hands, and produce greater comfort than regular-thickness bars. The thick handles also permit fine-tuning of hand positioning, for greater comfort.

Regardless of the type of set-up, the bars must be securely fixed so that they can't wobble as you dip.

Positioning

Find the strongest, most comfortable, and natural dipping position for you. Distribute the stress from the dip over all the involved muscles. Don't try to focus the stress on any one particular area.

Stand on a box or bench of the right height so that you can easily get into the elbows-locked-out position. When you bend your knees and descend into the dip, your shin just below your kneecaps should graze the box or bench when you're at your maximum safe depth. For most trainees, this is where the rear arm is parallel with the floor, or a little beneath that point. Some trainees can safely dip below the parallel position, whereas others need to stop a little above parallel.

To find a depth marker to suit you, try various benches or boxes. To fine-tune, place something of the correct thickness on top of the best-fit bench or box, preferably something with a soft surface.

Dipping so that your shins graze something set at your maximum safe depth isn't just to prevent overstretching. It ensures accurate records. Without a marker to ensure consistent depth, there's a tendency to shorten the reps at the end of a set.

Performance

Never bounce (or *pre-stretch* as it's sometimes called) at the bottom of the dip, and avoid doing reps rapidly. Go down slowly, pause for a second at the bottom, and push up in a controlled, smooth manner. Never relax at the bottom.

Keep your elbows in the same plane as your wrists, or slightly to the outside of that plane. Take a pause for a second between reps at the top position, but don't let your shoulders slump as you hold yourself on locked elbows. Keep your head and shoulders up high, and stay tight. Women in particular may find it uncomfortable to lock out fully. In such cases, stop the ascent just short of the fully locked out position.

Don't let your lower limbs swing as you dip, and neither thrust your head forward nor throw it back. Furthermore, keep your chest stuck out to help keep your shoulders pulled back and safe.

Never descend on a deflated chest. Inhale before you descend, then exhale during the ascent. Going into the bottom position of the dip on a deflated chest increases the risk of injury, so keep your chest full during the descent and early part of the ascent.

Three set-ups for the dip: unit with v-shaped bars (left), standing machine, seated machine.

an adjustable dumbbell. Alternatively, use individual weight plates with a belt fitted through them.

With the machine dip, a slight change in torso or wrist position can produce significant improvement in comfort, and the range of movement can be easily controlled. In addition, because resistance starts at little or nothing, the machine unit can be used by trainees who don't yet have the strength to do regular parallel bar dips.

Spotting

The main markers of technique deterioration are swinging lower limbs, throwing the head back, back arching, elbows wobbling, and stalling. The spotter should stand behind you. If you dip on bars attached to a wall, dip facing the wall so that your spotter has plenty of room. The spotter should place his hands under your shins—with your knees bent—and apply the minimum of assistance necessary if you require help to complete a rep.

Other tips

To warm up for the dip, start with floor push-ups. Then, from the upright position of the dip, perform partial reps as you gradually work into your bottom position. Then you would be ready for a work set. If you use a dip machine, matters are simpler, because you have full control over resistance.

For the non-machine dip, find a method of attaching weights comfortably and securely. Use of a purpose-made weight belt is the most common option. An alternative, at least for attaching small weights, is to wear a strong, leather belt used for trousers, and put a dumbbell inside it through having the 'bell vertical and the belt across the handle. Another option is to use strong rope to attach a dumbbell or plates to your belt. Let the resistance hang at the front of your thighs. If that's uncomfortable, suspend it from the rear. But it mustn't hang so low that it touches your depth marker before you reach your bottom position.

Strength permitting, add weight slowly and in small increments. To go from one fixed-weight dumbbell to the next, attach one or more small discs, or use

A purpose-made weight belt with attachments, for the parallel bar dip.

A shoulder harness isn't illustrated, but is the preferred option—for safety and comfort—if a substantial weight is to be attached to a suspended body. Otherwise, the forces pulling on the vertebrae may be excessive.

PRESS

The overhead press is usually called the *press*, without the *overhead* qualifier. When done standing, it's called the *military press*. The press can be done seated, to reduce the tendency to lean back. It can also be done seated against a high-incline bench, to remove much of the stress from the lower back—this is the most conservative form of the press, and what's recommended here.

The press behind neck is an unnatural movement that causes neck, shoulder, or rotator cuff problems for many trainees, and is best avoided. The press from the front is safer. If you find the barbell press awkward, use the dumbbell press instead.

Seated barbell press

Main muscles worked

deltoids, triceps, trapezius

Capsule description

while seated, push resistance from your shoulders to overhead

Set-up

Don't use a vertical bench. Use one set at about 75 to 80 degrees. Tilt the seat a little, if it's adjustable, to help prevent your slipping off the bench while pressing. Ensure any adjustable bench you use is sturdy, heavy, and stable.

Many gyms have purpose-built units for the seated barbell press, with fixed back support, and built-in uprights to hold the bar. Some can be good, but most have problems. The back support may be too upright, or too tall. Because the uprights that support the bar are usually behind the trainee, a spotter is essential for unracking and racking the bar. Taking the bar unassisted from behind your head is bad for your shoulders, and pressing from behind your neck can be harmful, too.

The seated press can be done in a power rack. Position the bench inside the rack so that you can't hit the uprights with the bar during a rep. Load the bar on pins set at the height from which you press.

You can also do the seated press close to squat stands. Position yourself and the stands so that you have minimum handling problems getting the barbell out of the stands to start a set, and returning it to the stands at the end of a set. Spotters should be used here so that you don't have to wrestle with the bar.

Don't use a machine that forces you to use a vertical bar pathway, such as a Smith machine. That will lock you into an unnatural groove that commonly leads to shoulder problems.

Positioning

When you're sat on the bench ready to press, your feet should be wider than shoulder width. Flare your feet for greater stability, and keep your heels directly beneath or slightly in front of an imaginary vertical line drawn through the middle of your knees.

The bottom position from where you press is typically at about the height of your clavicles (when you're in your pressing position), or a little higher (at, or just below chin height). For shoulder comfort, long-limbed trainees will need a slightly higher starting position than will short-limbed trainees. Starting too low will put excessive stress on the shoulder joints.

Take a pronated grip on the barbell. Start with a hand spacing two inches (five centimeters) wider on each side than your shoulder width, and fine-tune from there. Don't use a thumbless grip. Your forearms should be vertical at the bottom position of the press, when viewed from the front or rear.

Note the two flaws in this starting position for the seated press from the pins of a power rack. The elbows need to be moved forward to produce forearms nearer to vertical. And the lower spine shows exaggerated arching, largely because the heels are behind the knees.

Performance

Push the bar up vertically, and keep the rest of your body braced. Don't let the bar move forward. Push it up near your face, but be careful not to strike your face. Apply force evenly with both arms and shoulders. Don't let one hand get ahead of or in front of the other. Once the bar is above your head, allow it to travel two to three inches (five to eight centimeters) to the rear as it ascends, for a more natural pathway than a perfectly vertical one. Lock out your elbows smoothly, without jolting. Pause for a second at the top position.

Lower the bar under control, don't lower it beyond your safe point, and don't bounce at the bottom. Pause momentarily at the bottom before pushing the bar up, but don't relax at the bottom. Keep yourself tight, like a coiled spring.

During each press, keep a tight, full chest. Your chest mustn't collapse during the press. At the top of each rep, inhale fully to fill your chest, then immediately lower the bar under control. Take two to three seconds for the descent. To maintain the required tight, full chest, don't exhale until during the top half of the ascent, or until you've completed the ascent.

Keep a rigid wrist position during the press. Don't allow the weight to bend your hands backward more than just a little, because that can mar your lifting technique, and injure your wrists. Grip the bar firmly, to help keep your wrists in the right position.

Keep all your body's musculature tensed as you press and lower the bar, especially your legs, thighs, abdominals, buttocks, and back.

Back support height

If the back support from the bench is too tall, it won't allow your head to go back a little, out of the way of the barbell's ideal pathway. This would put the bar forward of the ideal pathway—to prevent striking your face—mar the exercise, and could produce injury because of poor distribution of stress. A shortened back support would be required. Alternatively, use dumbbells.

Spotting

At the end of a set of the press, the groove can easily be lost. The spotter should look out for the barbell tipping, one hand getting forward of the other, or the bar being pressed off center. The moment that one of those markers occurs, the spotter should provide assistance to prevent more serious technique deterioration.

The spotter should stand as close as possible behind the presser, to be able to apply assistance easily. The spotter must use both hands, apply help in a balanced way, and maintain a slightly arched back.

Caution

To help prevent back injuries while pressing, preserve a non-exaggerated hollow in your lower spine. This is the natural weight-bearing formation.

To avoid exaggerating the hollow in your lower spine while performing the seated press, keep your feet flat on the floor, with your heels directly beneath your knees, or a little in front of them.

Seated dumbbell press

Main muscles worked

deltoids, triceps, trapezius

Capsule description

while seated, push resistance from your shoulders to overhead

Dumbbell pressing can be done simultaneously, or by alternating hands. For the alternating dumbbell press, press with one hand as you lower with the other, or press and lower one dumbbell while the other waits at its shoulder. This produces asymmetrical stress and encourages leaning from side to side. Simultaneous pressing is safer.

Getting into position

Set up a bench with an incline of 75 to 80 degrees, and tilt its seat if it's adjustable. Then get the help of an assistant or, better yet, two assistants to hand you the dumbbells, or use the following method.

Stand just in front of a bench, feet about hip-width apart. Each dumbbell should touch the outside of its corresponding foot, with the handles parallel with each other. Bend your knees and take the 'bells with a parallel grip and correct deadlifting form. Because of the small-diameter plates, the range of motion when lifting dumbbells from the floor is considerable. Taking the 'bells off a rack or boxes is safer, provided good lifting technique is used.

While standing, center the rear end of each dumbbell on its corresponding thigh just above the knee. If you use dumbbells with protruding ends or collars—probably adjustable 'bells—place just the inside part of the bottom plate of a given dumbbell on the outside of its corresponding lower thigh. This will work if the radius of the dumbbell plate concerned is sufficient so that you can have the 'bell positioned vertically on your thigh while you're seated. The collars must be securely in place—a 'bell that falls apart during use could be disastrous.

Keep the dumbbells against your thighs, and sit on the bench, with your hips against the back support. The 'bells will move into a vertical position as you sit. The dumbbells must remain against your thighs, just above your knees.

Clockwise, from the bottom left, how to get into position for the seated dumbbell press without assistance, and the first ascent of the set.

Once you're sat on the bench, pause for a moment and then thrust your left knee up and simultaneously pull vigorously with your left arm. This will get the dumbbell to your left shoulder. Do the same for your right side.

Once you have the dumbbells at your shoulders, *roll* your back onto the back support—don't keep

Pressing from a parallel grip at the bottom position, to a pronated one at the top.

Before you do any dumbbell pressing, practice handling the 'bells.

The use of competent spotters will resolve the handling issue.

Performance

The dumbbell press allows you to find the wrist positioning and pressing groove that feel most comfortable for you. Your hands can be parallel with each other, pronated, or somewhere in between. Try each variation, and find the dumbbell pathway that feels the strongest and most comfortable for you. For example, start with your hands parallel with each other at shoulder height and, during the top half of the movement, move your hands to or toward a pronated position—see the illustration above.

an arched back as you lean backward. Now, you'll be in position for pressing, with your back supported.

When you've finished a set of dumbbell presses, move your feet and knees together, and lower the 'bells directly to the floor, quickly but under control. Keep the dumbbells well away from your legs and thighs. Alternatively, return the 'bells to your thighs using a reverse of the handling that got them to your shoulders. Control the 'bells—don't let them crash onto your thighs. Then stand and return the dumbbells to their rack.

Keep a rigid wrist position, and don't allow the weights to bend your hands backward more than just a little, because that can mar your lifting technique, and injure your wrists, too.

By permitting the natural positioning of your hands at the sides of your head, your head doesn't get in the way, unlike with a barbell.

Keep the dumbbells directly over your shoulders. Don't let them drift out to the sides, and don't overstretch at the bottom.

Push up smoothly from the bottom position, pause for a second at the top position, lower under control, pause momentarily at the bottom while keeping your entire body tight and tensed, then push smoothly into the next rep.

Follow the same breathing pattern that was prescribed for the barbell version.

Spotting

Spotting someone who's pressing dumbbells can be awkward. One hand should apply force under each elbow. This is strictly for assisting someone to get a tough rep up in correct technique.

A single person can't simultaneously take a pair of dumbbells from a presser who fails on a rep—two spotters are needed.

With dumbbell pressing, the key markers of technique regression to look out for are the 'bells drifting out to the sides, and one hand getting above, in front of, or to the rear of the other.

Caution

To help prevent back injuries while pressing, preserve a non-exaggerated hollow in your lower spine. This is the natural weight-bearing formation.

To avoid exaggerating the hollow in your lower spine, keep your feet flat on the floor, with your heels directly beneath your knees, or a little in front of them. If your feet are behind your knees, the arch will probably be exaggerated, and the risk of injury increased.

PULLDOWN

Main muscles worked

latissimus dorsi, upper back, pectorals, biceps, brachialis, forearms

Capsule description

sit beneath an overhead pulley, pull the bar to your chest

Set-up

Sit in the pulldown apparatus so that the cable runs vertically during the exercise, or sloped slightly toward you. A common mistake is to sit too far in the apparatus. Brace your thighs under the T-shaped restraint that has been set at the correct height for you.

Grip

There are several bar and grip options. Use the one that lets you use the most resistance over the fullest but safe range of motion. A supinated grip produces much more biceps involvement than the pronated grip.

With a straight bar, start with a supinated and shoulder-width grip, and fine-tune your hand spacing for wrist and elbow comfort. A hand spacing a little closer than shoulder-width may work best for the supinated grip.

For the parallel grip, a shoulder-width spacing produces a better effect than a close grip. Grip each handle in the center.

For the parallel grip and the supinated grip, use a hand spacing that keeps your forearms vertical during the exercise, provided that's safe for you.

The parallel grip results in a smaller weight potential than a supinated grip. Comparing the same range of motion, you'll need about 15% less weight with a parallel grip than a supinated one.

If a supinated grip is uncomfortable, even after having tried different hand spacings, and the bar for a shoulder-width,

parallel grip is unavailable, try a pronated grip using a straight bar. Take it two to three inches (five to eight centimeters) wider on each side than your shoulder-width grip, so that your forearms are vertical at the contracted position of the exercise.

Regardless of the bar you choose, avoid a wide grip, and don't pull to the rear of your head. Pulling to the rear is an unnatural action that puts unnecessary stress on the neck, cervical vertebrae, and shoulders. Pulling to the rear doesn't improve the muscle- and strength-building values of the pulldown, but increases the risk of injury.

Performance

Look forward or upward, and smoothly pull the bar until your hands are at your upper chest or a little lower, according to wrist and shoulder comfort.

During the descent, lean back only a little and arch your back slightly. Never round your back. If you have to round your back or crunch your abdominal muscles to help, the weight is too heavy. If you round your shoulders, you'll be unable to pull your shoulder blades down, and will rob yourself of working the target musculature properly.

If you can't pull your hands to below your clavicles, the weight is too heavy and you'll be unable to pull your shoulder blades down fully. Make a special effort to pull your shoulder blades down, but don't pull beyond what feels comfortable for your shoulders and elbows.

Pause for a second in the contracted position (at your chest), then let your elbows straighten

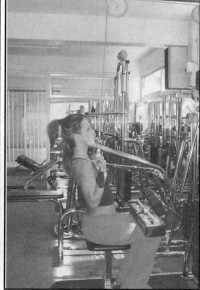

Correct performance of the pulldown, using a supinated grip.

smoothly and under control. The weight stack mustn't yank on any structure. Keep your shoulders tight when your arms are extended. Never relax in order to get extra stretch. Pause for a second at the top, then smoothly move into the next rep.

Look forward or slightly upward at all times, and keep your head in a neutral position—don't turn, crane, or extend your head. Exhale as you pull the bar down, and inhale as you straighten your elbows.

Use chalk or rosin on your hands when you need grip support. If the bar is smooth, chalk or rosin won't help you as much as they will with a bar that has knurling. To help your grip on a slick bar, put a palm-size piece of neoprene between each hand and the bar. Neoprene is a synthetic rubber with many uses. Get some small pieces from a scuba gear shop, an engineering storeroom on campus, or a hardware store.

Spotting

Spotting isn't essential here, because the weight can't come down on you. But spotting is desirable for ensuring that the final rep of a demanding set is done correctly. Technique starts to become ragged when your shoulders start to round. A spotter can push on the bar or pull on the weight stack.

Adding weight

Selectorized cable units, and selectorized machines in general, commonly have weight increments of 10 pounds or 5 kilos, and larger in some cases. This is too much to progress by in a single jump. Where you train may have special weights of 5 pounds or 2.5 kilos—and perhaps smaller ones, too—designed to fit on the top of a weight stack. If it doesn't, perhaps get your own from an exercise equipment store. Use them to help you to work from one pin setting to the next.

Alternatively, place the weight selection pin through a small barbell weight plate before the pin goes into the weight stack. Although a pin that holds a plate won't go fully into the weight stack, it should go through enough to hold the plate securely and select the resistance, too.

Magnetic small plates are another option for adding small increments to a weight stack.

Whichever option you choose, check that the set-up is secure before you perform a set.

Common errors in the pulldown.

RADER CHEST PULL

Main structure worked

rib cage

This exercise was developed by Peary Rader.

This is a stretching and forced breathing exercise that may enlarge your rib cage, deepen your chest, and help to improve your posture. It—or its alternative, the *breathing pullover*—is a mainstay of **Course #1**.

It may be especially effective for teenagers, and trainees in their early twenties, but is worth a try at any age. There's no science to confirm this, however. I believe the breathing pullover helped me, and other people have reported benefits, too.

Stand at about arm's length from a vertical bar, with your feet hip-width apart. Alternatively, use a sturdy, stable object that can be grasped at about head height. An upright on a power rack, or a door jamb, will do the job. If you use an upright of a power rack, or a vertical bar, keep your hands together. If you use another object, keep your hands close together.

While keeping your arms straight, take a deep breath and simultaneously pull down *and in* with your arms. Don't contract your abdominal muscles. Keep them relaxed. If you tense your abs, this will flatten your chest and defeat the purpose of the exercise. Done correctly, the Rader chest pull will raise your chest and produce a pull and slight discomfort in your sternum. If you don't feel this, you're not doing the exercise properly.

You may get a better effect if you bend your arms *slightly*, because this will let you pull harder. The harder you pull, the better the effect on your rib cage, so long as you're pulling in the right way.

Rader recommended that you tense the muscles at the front of your neck and then pull your head back. This should be done at the same time as you pull down *and in* with your arms. This neck involvement provides further stretching and lifting of your rib cage. But don't apply this tip until after you've learned to apply the other instruction.

Once you get to grips with it you'll feel a pronounced stretch in your rib cage. It may take a while to get the exercise right. You may have to fine-tune the height you have your hands, the spacing between your hands, the distance between your feet and the base of the object you hold, and the angle of pull. Persist until you get it right.

Hold your breath for as long as comfortable, and throughout the entire time you should be able to feel the pull and slight discomfort in your sternum. Don't, however, hold your breath until you're almost ready to burst, because you need to be able to perform up to 20 reps for a single set. How long you can comfortably hold your breath will depend on the state of your breathing prior to performing the chest pull, and your general conditioning. With practice, over time, you'll be able to hold each pull for a longer time, for a comparable level of discomfort. Somewhere in the range of four to six seconds per pull will be fine.

The Rader chest pull is traditionally done immediately after an exercise that gets you heavily winded, such as the squat, especially when the latter's done for high reps. And it can be done at other times, too. It's not systemically demanding work, and neither is the breathing pullover.

Go easy at the beginning. The forced and exaggerated breathing may make you feel dizzy unless you work into it progressively over a few weeks. Your chest may get sore, too, if you don't work into the exercise gradually.

Starting position of the Rader chest pull.

ROW

Four rows will be described: the one-arm dumbbell row, the cable row, the machine row, and the prone low-incline dumbbell row.

There are other rows, including the barbell row, and the t-bar row, both of which are fraught with danger. They don't have the body supported, the lower back is excessively involved, it's difficult to keep the lower spine hollow and secure once the weight becomes substantial—just a slight slip in technique can produce lower-back injury—and the wrist positioning they impose isn't ideal.

One-arm dumbbell row

Main muscles worked

latissimus dorsi, upper back, biceps, brachialis, rear deltoid, forearms

Capsule description

with one hand braced on a bench, take a dumbbell and pull it to your obliques

Stand next to a bench (or something stable of a similar height), with a dumbbell on the floor at your left side. Bend over and brace your right hand on the bench. Your right knee should be bent and your right foot well ahead of your left. Alternatively, your right knee could be placed on the bench. Either way, your left knee should be almost straight, and your torso inclined somewhat, as illustrated. Keep your lower spine slightly hollow throughout the exercise.

With your left hand, grab the dumbbell from the floor, with the handle parallel with your spine. Keep your elbow in, and smoothly pull the dumbbell as high as possible at your left oblique, or hip (depending on your body structure, and what feels comfortable for you). Pull in an arc, not a straight line. Don't yank the dumbbell up, don't rotate about your spine, and don't twist your torso. Only move your hand, forearm, arm, and shoulder.

Hold the top position for a second, and crush your shoulder blades together. At the top position, your elbow should be well above the height of your spine.

Top left, correct starting position. Top right, incorrect finish. Middle, correct technique. Above, alternative set-up using a low-incline bench— probably the pick of the three variations of the one-arm row—and correct technique.

On the descent, smoothly retrace the arc of the ascent. At the bottom, pause for a second without relaxing or putting the dumbbell on the floor, then smoothly move into the next rep. Your forearm should be vertical or almost-vertical throughout the exercise. Inhale during the descent or while your elbow is straight, and exhale on the ascent.

This method works your left side. To train your right side, reverse the procedure.

To reduce the size of the weight jumps between fixed-weight dumbbells, use the same approach described for the *Dumbbell bench press.* But in the dumbbell row, use of wrist weights (obtainable from a sporting goods store) may be a good option for progressively working from one fixed-weight 'bell to the next. The wrist weights shouldn't spoil your balance in the dumbbell row, unlike in pressing movements.

Cable row

Main muscles worked

latissimus dorsi, upper back, biceps, brachialis, rear deltoid, forearms

Capsule description

while seated, pull to your waist or lower chest a bar fixed to a cable running from a low pulley

Set-up and positioning

Use a shoulder-width supinated grip on a straight bar, a shoulder-width (or slightly wider) pronated grip on a straight bar or, better still, use a shoulder-width parallel grip on a special bar. One of the most common mistakes in this exercise is doing it with hands too close. A shoulder-width grip produces a better effect than a narrow one, because it keeps the forearms parallel and in a more natural position.

For the parallel grip, encourage the management where you train to get a shoulder-width bar if it doesn't already have one. If you're unsuccessful, buy your own bar, or get one custom made and take it with you when you're scheduled to do this exercise. Aim for a grip spacing that keeps your forearms parallel with each other throughout the exercise. Grasp each handle in the center.

Sit on the floor, or on the built-in low seat, with your feet against the foot restraint. If there isn't a foot restraint, improvise so that you have a foot brace that lets you space your feet as required.

The starting position has you seated with your torso vertical, lower spine slightly hollow, elbows pulled out straight by the resistance, knees slightly bent. To get into that position, bend your knees sufficiently so that you can take the handle with your back in the correct starting position. Then maintain the correct back positioning and straighten your knees sufficiently so that you won't bang them with the bar during the exercise. Keep your knees bent to some degree, to help you maintain the right back positioning.

Some cable row set-ups have cables that are too short, and it's difficult to get into the starting position. There's even the risk of injury while getting into position. If you use a selectorized pulldown apparatus, you may be able to adjust the weight stack so that the bar is precisely where you want it for the starting position.

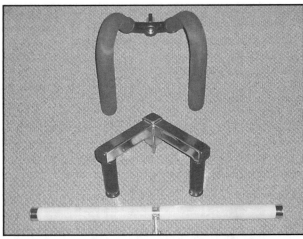

Close-parallel-grip bars are commonly used in the cable row, but such a grip is inferior to a shoulder-width one. A shoulder-width parallel grip is the ideal. The bottommost photograph shows an adjustable, parallel-grip bar—a single-width grip won't suit all users.

Use a shoulder-width pronated grip, or a shoulder-width supinated grip, as the alternative to the ideal of the shoulder-width parallel grip. Try both, to find which feels the most comfortable.

To delimit the range of motion manually, remove the pin from the weight stack, then grip the cable that's attached to the guide rod that runs through the weight stack, and lift it. The top weight plate will rise alone, revealing the guide rod. Expose two holes on the rod, for example, then use the pin to select the required weight. The gap between the first and second weight plates indicates the reduction in range of motion. Fine-tune the extent of the reduction according to what's required to produce the maximum safe range of motion for you. Make a note in your training log of the setting.

This procedure for delimiting the range of motion can be used for other selectorized machines, too.

But for a large adjustment, extra chain between the bar and cable may be required.

Performance

Smoothly pull the bar into your upper abdomen or lower chest, according to what feels most natural for you according to the lengths of your torso,

How to delimit manually the range of motion using a selectorized weight stack. See text.

forearms, and arms. Keep your forearms parallel with the floor, and don't let your elbows drift out to the sides. Your elbows should be equally spaced throughout each rep. Arch your back slightly as you crush your shoulder blades together, but don't lean back. Your elbows mustn't rise when you're in the contracted position—keep your forearms parallel with the floor. Hold the contraction for a second, then let the resistance pull your elbows straight in a controlled manner. Pause for a second in the starting position, don't relax your shoulders, then smoothly move into the next rep.

Keep your torso upright and rigid throughout each rep. Imagine that your torso is supported, and can't move.

Each phase of a rep should take two to three seconds, plus an additional second for holding the contracted position, and another second at the starting position.

Other tips

If you lean back beyond the vertical, at least with a demanding weight, you'll round your shoulders, be unable to crush your shoulder blades together, and rob yourself of working the target muscles.

Don't relax your shoulders between reps, to permit a full stretch. A full stretch puts great stress on the rotator cuff muscles at the back of your shoulders, and will set you up for an injury. Keep your shoulders tight.

Look forward or slightly upward at all times, and keep your head in a neutral position—don't turn, crane, or extend your head.

Use chalk or rosin on your hands when you need grip support. If the bar is smooth, chalk or rosin won't help you as much as they will with a bar that

The top two photographs show correct technique, using a pronated, shoulder-width grip on a straight bar. The next one shows incorrect technique—raised elbows, and rounded back— but using the especially recommended parallel, shoulder-width grip. The bottom photograph shows improved technique, but there's still some rearward lean that should be avoided.

has knurling. To help your grip on a slick bar, put a palm-size piece of neoprene between each hand and the bar. Neoprene is a synthetic rubber with many uses. Get some small pieces from a scuba gear shop, an engineering storeroom on campus, or a hardware store.

Spotting

Spotting isn't essential here, because the resistance can't come down on you. Technique becomes ragged when your shoulders start to slump. Immediately, a spotter should pull on the weight stack cable just enough to enable you to get the rep out in correct technique.

Adding weight

Selectorized cable units, and selectorized machines in general, commonly have weight increments of 10 pounds or 5 kilos, and larger in some cases. This is too much to progress by in a single jump. Where you train may have special weights of 5 pounds or 2.5 kilos—and perhaps smaller ones, too—designed to fit on the top of a weight stack. If it doesn't, perhaps get your own from an exercise equipment store. Use them to help you to work from one pin setting to the next.

Alternatively, place the weight selection pin through a small barbell weight plate before the pin goes into the weight stack. Although a pin that holds a plate won't go fully into the weight stack, it should go through enough to hold the plate securely and select the resistance, too.

Magnetic small plates are another option for adding small increments to a weight stack.

Whichever option you choose, check that the set-up is secure before you perform a set.

Seated machine row

Main muscles worked

latissimus dorsi, upper back, biceps, brachialis, rear deltoid, forearms

Capsule description

sit and pull the handles to your waist or lower chest

This exercise is similar to the cable row, but with a simpler set-up. Furthermore, the chest is braced against a pad, which prevents the lower back from fatiguing, and thus increases stability and safety.

There may also be a foot bar, to help increase stability further. If there isn't, place your feet on the floor in front of you, wider than hip-width.

Depending on the machine, you may have the choice between a pronated grip, a supinated grip, and a parallel grip. A parallel grip of shoulder-width is ideal.

If the parallel-grip handles are a lot closer than shoulder-width, use a pronated grip (palms down, in this case) of shoulder-width or a little wider, depending on comfort. A supinated grip (palms up, in this case) may feel comfortable, or it may irritate your wrists and elbows, depending on the positioning of the handles.

Adjust the seat's height to find the position that permits you to have your forearms parallel with the floor when you're in the contracted position.

Pull your elbows as far behind you as possible, but keep your chest on the pad. Crush your shoulder blades together, hold the contraction, then let the resistance pull your elbows straight in a controlled manner. Pause in the starting position, don't relax your shoulders, then smoothly move into the next rep.

Keep your torso against the chest pad throughout each set, and your back slightly arched.

Take two to three seconds to pull the handles to your torso (the positive phase), pause for a second in the contracted position with your scapulae fully retracted, take two to three seconds for the negative phase, and a further second in the starting position.

Prone low-incline dumbbell row

This two-arm dumbbell row is an alternative to the one-arm variation described earlier in this section. It's also an alternative to the cable row, and the machine row. Illustrated is the starting position. You may need to move your knees further to the rear, so that they aren't struck by the dumbbells during the ascent. Follow the same pathway and control guidelines as for the one-arm dumbbell row.

To demonstrate exercise technique clearly, the models sometimes didn't wear shirts, and weight stands and safety bars were often not used. This was for illustration purposes only. When you train, wear a shirt, and take proper safety measures.

SHRUG

Main muscles worked

trapezius, deltoids, forearms

Capsule description

while holding resistance, with straight elbows, shrug your shoulders

There are several types of shrugs, including upright, incline, and prone.

Set-up, and performance

Use your bench press hand spacing, or slightly wider. A close grip, or moving quickly, will prompt your elbows to bend. With a pronated grip, keep your elbows rotated inward, to lock your elbows.

Use a pronated grip on a straight bar with deep knurling, and chalk or rosin on your hands when you need grip support. Only when you need further grip support should you use a reverse grip. But as with the partial deadlift (or any type of deadlift with a straight bar) using a mixed grip in the straight-bar shrug results in a tendency to twist somewhat, and produce an asymmetrical motion.

To balance out this rotational effect, and reduce injury potential, alternate from set to set which way around you have the mixed grip. Even if you find one way around to be more favorable than the other, still work it the other way around, too.

To offset the rotational effect, experiment with having your supinated hand one to two inches (two to five centimeters) nearer the center of the bar than your pronated hand.

With a parallel-grip bar, or dumbbells, deep knurling is also required. Use chalk or rosin, too, when you need additional grip support.

Regardless of which equipment you use, and for reasons explained in the section on the parallel-grip deadlift, when you place the bar or handles in your hands, place it (or them) against the part of your palm right at the base of your fingers, not in the center of your palms.

Three standing shrugs: barbell (left), dumbbell (middle), parallel-grip-bar (right). The parallel-grip-bar shrug illustrations show bending of the elbows. The elbows should be straight.

Stand, with your elbows straight, and hold a bar as if you were in the top position of a deadlift. Without bending your elbows, smoothly shrug as high as possible—try to raise your shoulders to your ears—and pause for a second. Lower under control, pause for a second without relaxing, and repeat.

As an alternative to taking equipment from the floor for each set, place a barbell over pins set in a power rack at your bottom position, or, place a loaded barbell, parallel-grip bar, or dumbbells on boxes of the appropriate height. Position the dumbbells one at a time. You may need an assistant to help you set up the equipment.

Keep your body tight, a slight arch in your lower spine (don't round your back), don't shuffle your feet around, and don't take more of the stress on one side of your body than the other. Keep the stress distributed symmetrically.

Dumbbells and a parallel-grip bar are ideal for the upright shrug. They aren't obstructed by your thighs or hips, unlike a straight bar. Use a parallel grip in the dumbbell shrug, with your hands by the sides of your thighs and hips.

The barbell shrug and parallel-grip-bar shrug are performed standing only. The dumbbell shrug can be done seated, too, at the end of a bench.

Caution

Don't use a circular action when shrugging, because it places unnecessary wear on the shoulder joints. Furthermore, keep your shoulders tight at the bottom of each rep—don't let the weight yank your shoulders.

A common error is to stretch the head forward during the ascent. This can lead to neck and trapezius injuries. During upright shrugs, keep your head in an upright, neutral position.

The seated incline dumbbell shrug is an alternative to the regular shrug, although some trainees may find the compression of the chest uncomfortable.

Position an adjustable bench at the lowest setting that, when you're face down, allows you to keep your elbows straight and take dumbbells off the floor without forcing a stretch.

While in position on the bench, shrug your shoulders and pull them back. Crush your shoulder blades together, then lower the dumbbells under control to the floor, pause for a second, and then start the next rep.

Don't jam your chin onto the bench.

Calf machine shrug—*danger*

For this form of the standing shrug, the resistance rests against the actual musculature that's primarily worked by the exercise. When the musculature contracts, it's distorted because of the compression from the weight. This produces a skewed effect on the musculature, and leads to possible tissue damage. The musculature being worked should be free of compressive impediment to its contraction and relaxation.

The negative effect of the calf machine shrug on the trapezius depends on the design of the calf machine, and the body structure of the individual trainee. There'll probably be a severe pull at the base of the skull regardless of the size of the user or design of the machine. Avoid the calf machine shrug. Use another type of shrug.

SIDE BEND

Main muscles worked

abdominal wall including the quadratus lumborum, erector spinae

Capsule description

hold resistance against a thigh, bend to that side, and return upright

The side bend also provides direct work for some of the small, intervertebral muscles. The side bend works most of the body's core musculature.

The side bend is an asymmetrical exercise. So long as you have a healthy spine free of restrictions, the side bend, when performed correctly, will strengthen your body's core muscles, and increase their resistance to injury. If, however, your spinal musculature has restrictions, the side bend will probably be a harmful, and should be avoided.

Perform the side bend with a dumbbell, or a cable from a low pulley.

Dumbbell side bend

Space your feet a little wider than hip-width, but fine-tune this to suit you. If you have a tendency toward groin strains, a closer stance may be better. But balance and stability may be harder to maintain with a close stance than a wider one. Keep your buttocks contracted.

A simpler way of doing the dumbbell side bend is while seated at the end of a bench, across the middle of a bench with one foot on each side, or on a box. With a wide enough foot placement to maintain balance, this variation can work well. There's no problem with the plates striking your thighs and obstructing performance.

Performance

Take the weight in your right hand. Rest your left hand on your left hip, or external oblique. Bend to your right side as far as is comfortable, pause for a second, then return to the vertical position and continue as far as is comfortable to the left, for a full range of motion across both sides. Pause for a second, then repeat. In the standing side bend, as

you bend to your right, push your hips to your left, and vice versa. This may help improve stability, and increase the range of motion, too. As you return to the vertical position, move your torso first, *then* your hips. Do all your reps to your right side without interruption. To exercise the other side of your body, reverse the procedure.

The range of motion could have been increased had the model moved his hips to his left during the descent to his right side, and then continued over to his left side at the top position of the rep. And a wider stance would give greater stability.

Face forward throughout each set. There should be lateral movement only. Don't lean forward, don't lean backward, and don't overstretch.

For stability, keep the distribution of weight over your feet to as near as possible a 50-50 split.

While you perform the standing side bend, as you descend you should take more of the stress on the inner sides of your feet than the outer.

Do the reps carefully—about three seconds up, and three seconds down, plus a pause for a second at the top, and another at the bottom. Use smooth, controlled movements. Inhale on the descent, and exhale on the ascent, or just breathe freely.

Dumbbell seated side bend. A wider spacing of the feet would give increased stability.

Pulley side bend

Use a cable that arises from a low pulley. Stand sideways to the apparatus, with the handle in your hand that's nearest to the apparatus. Stand a sufficient distance away so that the plates can't come to rest at the bottom position. And line up the pulley with your ankle, and the direction of the cable with the center of the side of your hips, to keep the resistance in the same plane as your body.

The lowest position, left, could be increased if the trainee's hips were pushed to her left during the descent to her right. The middle shot shows the usual completion point. But each rep can be continued by bending over toward the other side, for further range of motion (right photograph).

Then follow the guidelines for the dumbbell standing side bend.

Other tips

After an intensive set of side bends, take two to three minutes rest before working your other side, so that your performance on the latter doesn't suffer. From workout to workout, alternate the side you work first.

Carefully adapt to side bend if you've not done it before, or if you've not done it for a long time. For two weeks, do it two times a week without added resistance. Do a couple of sets of high reps each time. Keep your hands by your sides, then progress to placing them on top of your head. Focus on smooth, controlled reps. Go down to a depth that feels comfortable. If your flexibility increases, you may be able to increase the depth a little during the first few weeks.

Have an assistant watch you from the side, to see if you make any forward movement. Ingrain lateral movement only.

In your third week of side bends, use a light weight and thereafter add poundage gradually, using small increments.

When you take the resistance to get set up for the side bend—whether a dumbbell, or from a low pulley—keep the stress as symmetrical as possible. Bend your knees, keep your shoulders pulled back, lower spine slightly hollow, and brace your disengaged hand against the thigh on the same side, while the engaged hand takes the resistance from the other side. And reverse the procedure at the end of a set, when you return the resistance to the floor.

Ideally, for the dumbbell side bend, take the 'bell from a dumbbell rack, and set it on a bench or a box rather than the floor. Then you would need to bend your knees only slightly in order to take the dumbbell with one hand. Then adopt your stance ready to start a set. At the end of a set, put the dumbbell back on the bench or box while you rest prior to the next set.

SQUAT

Only two forms of the squat are described here—barbell back squat, and hip-belt squat—because only those variations are employed in **Course #1**:

There are, however, two basic forms of the barbell squat—back squat, and front squat. The front squat has the bar held at the front of the shoulders, whereas the back squat has the bar held on the upper back. The front squat always has the *front* qualifier, whereas the back squat is usually called *the squat* without the *back* qualifier. There's no tradition of using the front squat in **Course #1**—the front squat isn't as well suited to heavy, high-rep, rest-pause squatting as the back squat is.

If you've had a serious back injury, don't squat without the clearance of a chiropractor. If you've had any minor back injuries, still get a chiropractor's clearance.

Squats, knees, and lower back

Forward travel of the knees is inevitable while squatting, but should be minimized, to reduce stress on the knees. A common guideline for squatting is, during the descent, to avoid the knees traveling forward beyond an imaginary vertical line drawn from the toes. But few people can follow it for barbell squatting unless they perform partial squats only. Use of your fullest *safe* range of motion—safe for your lower back *and* for your knees—is recommended, and this will probably mean that your knees will travel forward of your toe line during the barbell squat. Some competitive powerlifters squat with almost vertical shins. They can do this because they have favorable leverages for the squat, use a wide stance, and exaggerate the involvement of their lower backs, and hips. Their goal is to increase their one-rep maximum performances.

The recommendation in this book is to descend until about two inches or five centimeters above the point at which your lower back would start to round. Your back must never round while squatting. For some bodybuilders, this range of motion means that the top of the upper thighs at the bottom position is just *below* parallel with the floor—the "full squat." This is the ideal. For some other bodybuilders, the maximum safe range of motion is to where the top of the upper thighs is parallel with the floor—the "parallel squat." But for some others, the maximum safe range of motion is to *above* the parallel position—in those cases, an alternative linchpin exercise should be used.

Don't give up on the barbell squat because of initial difficulties. After you've become supple, and truly mastered squatting technique, you should be able to squat more effectively (and deeper) than you can now. This section will teach you how to squat.

Correct technique to minimize forward travel of the knees while barbell squatting, includes:

1. Wearing a pair of shoes with no heel, or only minimal heel.

2. Not elevating your heels on plates, or a board.

3. Turning the toes of each foot out to between about 20 to 30 degrees from the feet-parallel-to-each-other position.

4. Keeping the sense of the weight mostly over your heels—*not* over the balls of your feet.

While applying these guidelines, you must maintain a slight hollow in your lower spine, and minimize forward lean of your torso. But some forward lean is necessary while barbell squatting.

If, however, after having tried your best to master the barbell squat you still can't perform it properly to the parallel position (or, better still, to just below parallel), it will be time to try the alternatives—the parallel-grip deadlift, and the hip-belt squat.

Remember that the hip-belt squat puts very little loading on the back, and keeps the stress primarily on the thighs and hips. It requires a special set-up but not a special bar. Of the three linchpin exercises, the hip-belt squat is by far the simplest to perform, and thus has the lowest risk.

Provided all three are done properly, the barbell squat and the parallel-grip deadlift are the more effective overall muscle builders because each involves more musculature than the hip-belt squat. But if you truly can't barbell squat or parallel-grip deadlift as required, make the hip-belt squat your sole linchpin exercise.

Footwear reminder

Especially for squats, deadlifts, and overhead presses, you shouldn't wear shoes with thick or spongy soles and heels.

Get sturdy shoes with good grip to the floor, and arch support, and which minimize deformation when you're lifting heavy weights. Little or no heel elevation relative to the balls of your feet is especially important for squats and deadlifts.

Safety equipment

It's imperative that you can never be pinned or crushed by a weight, even if you train alone.

Barbell squat inside a four-post power rack with pins and saddles correctly and securely in place. Alternatively, use a half rack, sturdy and stable squat stands together with spotter racks or bars, or a squat rack unit that combines stands and safety bars. For example, position the pins—or safety bars—an inch or two centimeters below your bottom point of the squat. Then if you can't perform a rep, lower the bar under control to the pins, get out from under the bar, remove the plates, and return the bar to its holders.

A power rack, correctly used, is perfect for self-spotting, and safety, and can be found in some gyms. It's especially useful for barbell squats, barbell bench press and its variations, deadlifts, and barbell presses.

There must be no compromise here—safety comes first. Ideally, you should have spotters standing by in addition to the aforementioned safety set-up.

The uprights of power racks typically have about two inches or five centimeters between successive holes. If one setting is too high, and the next too low, raise the floor. For the squat, place non-slip rubber matting of the right thickness throughout the floor space within the rack (so that there's no chance of tripping on the edge of the matting).

A four-post power rack and its accessories: two adjustable barbell saddles (on the rear uprights), four pins or safety bars (on the floor), four small locking pins (on the base) for fixing the safety bars in the rack's uprights, and two lengths of hose for putting over the safety bars to help prevent the barbell slipping when on the pins. A power rack is sometimes called a power cage.

A squat rack (top), and an "open" rack (left). Squat racks are common in gyms, but many have fixed-height safety bars, whereas the one illustrated has safety bars that can be adjusted for height. The "open" rack is fully adjustable.

How to improve your ability to barbell squat

Only a small proportion of bodybuilders are naturally gifted for barbell squatting, largely because of their body proportions and leverages. Most bodybuilders need to work at squatting technique and the essential supportive work, to make themselves into competent squatters.

There are three major components of good barbell squatting ability:

1. The flexibility to be able to adopt the correct body positioning.

2. The back strength to be able to maintain the correct back positioning.

3. Correct exercise technique.

You need sufficient flexibility in the major musculature of your lower body, along with the required shoulder flexibility to hold the bar in position correctly. Follow the stretching routine in this book. If any of the muscles have anything less than at least a normal, healthy level of flexibility, squatting technique will probably be compromised, with a reduction in safety and productivity. Squat correctly, or not at all.

You need sufficient strength throughout your back—lower, middle, and upper—to be able to hold your lower spine in the required slightly hollow position during the squat, which is critical for safety. Your back mustn't round while squatting—there must be no back flexion. Three key back exercises—partial deadlift, row, and shrug—will help build the required back strength provided that they are worked with correct technique, and progressively ever-greater resistance.

Having the required flexibility and back strength is one thing, but learning to use the flexibility and strength during the squat is something else.

It may take several weeks if not a couple of months before correct barbell squatting technique can be implemented, even with minimal weight. Don't be frustrated to begin with. Be patient. As your flexibility and back strength improve, along with your ability to use them, so will your squatting ability. Until you can adopt the correct technique, keep the resistance very light. Thereafter, as your squat poundage grows, so should your strength in the deadlift, row, and shrug, to help you maintain the correct back positioning.

Proper assessment of depth, and back positioning

To accurately determine your depth of squatting, and your back positioning at the bottom of the exercise, get an assistant to watch you from the side (while crouched, to view you from about your knee height), and provide you with instant feedback. You can't see what's happening in those areas from the reflection in a mirror in front of you, and you shouldn't watch yourself in a side-on mirror while you exercise.

Barbell back squat

Main muscles worked

quadriceps, thigh adductors, buttocks, hamstrings, spinal erectors, multifidii

Capsule description

hold a barbell over your upper back, squat, then stand erect

Set-up

Apply the safety precautions explained earlier in this section. There have been terrible injuries among bodybuilders who squatted without a safety set-up, or spotters standing by. For example, when they failed on a rep, they got crushed by the weight before they dumped it, or they toppled forward and severely injured their backs.

A straight bar is fine for squatting, especially for lower-rep work, but a cambered squat bar is better—especially for high reps. A cambered bar is curved. Relative to a straight bar, the bent bar is easier to hold in position, sits better on the upper back, and is less likely to roll out of position. A camber of as little as just one inch in a barbell is sufficient to make a big difference, but a little larger camber may be better still.

A cambered bar is highly recommended.

Encourage the management of where you train to get a cambered squat bar. A skilled metal worker can put a camber in a straight bar.

Straight or cambered, if the bar you use for the squat has knurling around its center, that will help you to keep it in position during a set.

If you can't squat correctly with a straight bar, a bent bar may not make enough difference to warrant the investment. But if you can squat correctly with a straight bar, you'll probably be able to squat even better with a cambered bar, especially for high reps.

Set the bar on its saddles at mid- to upper-chest height. If the bar is too low, you'll waste energy getting it out. If it's too high, you'll need to rise on your toes to get the bar out. The too-high setting is especially dangerous when you return the bar after finishing a hard set of squats.

If you're used to squatting with a straight bar, and move to a cambered bar, you must lower the position of the saddles and that of the pins or safety bars at the bottom position of the squat. The ends of a cambered bar are lower than the central part that rests on your upper back.

Use little or preferably no padding on the bar. If you're a novice you'll probably have little visible muscle over your upper back. After a few months of progressively heavier training that includes deadlifts and shrugs, you'll start developing the muscular padding required there. Then the bar can be held in position more comfortably.

The more padding that's around a bar, the more likely that the bar will be incorrectly positioned, or that it will move during a set. Wear a thick sweatshirt rather than a thin T-shirt, to provide acceptable padding to cushion the bar. If more padding is needed, wear a T-shirt and a sweatshirt. The clothing should be cotton, to prevent slickness when sweaty. Avoid tank tops and vests because they cover less skin. Skin is slick when sweaty, but a barbell won't stay in place if it's on a slick surface.

Your shorts or other training bottoms should be made from a material that stretches.

Bar positioning

Locate the spine of your scapulae or shoulder blades. Place your right hand on the side of your left hip. Keep it there as you reach with your left hand above and over your right shoulder. Reach down and place that hand on your right shoulder blade. Feel for the prominent diagonal ridge of bone. That's the spine of that scapula.

Dip under the bar. But before you position the bar on your back, crush your shoulder blades together. This creates a layer of tensed muscle on your upper back. Then position the bar on the muscle

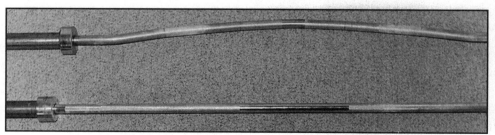

Cambered squat bar (top), and a straight barbell. This bent bar has a camber of 2.75 inches, but a camber of just one inch can be enough to make a big difference.

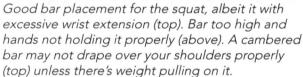

Good bar placement for the squat, albeit it with excessive wrist extension (top). Bar too high and hands not holding it properly (above). A cambered bar may not drape over your shoulders properly (top) unless there's weight pulling on it.

immediately above the center of the spine of your shoulder blades. This is lower than what's typically used by most bodybuilders, but as low as is probably practical for high-rep squatting. Some low-rep squatters put the bar lower still, if they have the required suppleness.

The correct bar position is essential—to avoid metal to vertebrae contact, and to provide a greater area of contact than that from a higher position. This yields greater bar control.

Practice correct bar positioning until you can do it automatically. What may initially feel awkward, will become relatively comfortable after a few weeks.

Grip

Hold the bar securely in your hands (not loosely in the tips of your fingers), with minimal wrist extension. Each hand must be equidistant from the center of the bar. Don't drape your wrists over the bar, or your hands over the plates.

Hold the bar in position so that your *back* carries the entire load. Don't carry any of the load with your hands, wrists or arms.

Top left, feet far too close. Above, feet well spaced but with too little flare. Left, this stance, or something close to it, will work well for most bodybuilders.

The bar is too high in these three photos, and the back isn't properly set because the model is focusing on tensing his abs.

The width of grip depends on torso size, forearm and arm lengths, and shoulder and pec flexibility. Use the closest grip that feels comfortable. You may need to start with a grip a little wider than ideal. As your flexibility increases, narrow your grip.

If your grip is too wide, you'll risk trapping your fingers between the bar and the safety supports or rack pins at the bottom of the squat. A too-wide grip also diminishes the thickness of the tensed muscle that the bar rests on.

Stance

In order to find the stance that works best for you, you need to experiment somewhat. But before you

The left-side photos show the correct stance—heels well spaced, and toes flared. The right-side photos show an incorrect stance—feet close together, and parallel with each other. Note how the incorrect stance increases forward travel of the knees, and forward lean of the torso.

The bar is positioned too high in these photos; and there's excessive wrist extension, which can lead to wrist problems.

can do that, you must know how to perform the entire squat motion. So read the entire section on the barbell squat, and then set about the experimentation that follows.

Using a bare bar (or even just a broomstick), find your optimum width of heel placement, and degree of toe flare. As a starting point, place your feet hip-width apart and parallel with each other, then turn out the toes on each foot about 30 degrees. Perform some squats, ideally to just below the position where the top of your upper thighs is just below parallel to the floor. Have an assistant crouch at your side to guide you on depth. Then try a little wider stance with the initial toe flare, and then with

a little less flare. But don't overdo your heel spacing—too wide will hinder you. And try with your heels slightly narrower than hip-width but with the wider flare. Try all the permutations of width and flare until you find what you think is best for you.

It's essential that you shove your knees out on each descent, so that your knees point in the same direction as your feet. This produces a wider knee position than most bodybuilders use. Your knees must never buckle inward.

The combination of a moderately spaced stance and well-flared toes usually gives plenty of room to squat into, helps to prevent excessive forward lean, and lets you squat deeper without your lower back rounding. Individual variation in leg and thigh lengths and flexibility, natural foot angle or flare, torso length, hip width, and relative lengths of legs and thighs, contribute to determining the stance that's ideal for you. Tall bodybuilders usually need a wider stance than those of average height.

If you have a stance that's too close, or has insufficient toe flare, then buckling of your knees may be inevitable when you squat intensively.

It may take a few workouts before you find the best stance for you. With just a bare bar over your upper back, stand on some cardboard, and adopt your squat stance. Do a few squats, tinker with your stance until you think it's correct, then get someone to draw the outline of your feet on the card. Then you'll have a record of your stance for when you want to refer to it. Practice repeatedly until you can adopt your squat stance automatically. Include practice at home, using a broomstick instead of a barbell.

But as you progress in the squat, you may want to tweak your stance further, to help you improve your overall technique.

Initial performance

Face the bar so that you have to walk *backward* from the saddles before taking your squatting stance. Take your grip on the bar, and get under it as it rests on the weight saddles or stands. Don't lean over to get under the bar. Bend your knees, and get your torso and hips underneath the bar. Your feet can either be hip-width apart under the bar, or split. If split, one foot will be a little in front of the bar, and the other will be a little behind it.

Then crush your scapulae together and lift your chest, tense the musculature of your back, and position the bar correctly. (Your lower spine should be slightly hollow, and your hips directly under the

The above right photograph (of the bottom position) shows the error of shifting stress from mostly over the rear of the feet, to mostly over the balls of the feet. This has resulted in heel lifting, reduced stability, and exaggerated load on the knees. The model is wearing shoes with thick heels, which may have contributed to the technique error. And furthermore, there's excessive neck extension during the motion.

Safety bars/pins

The safety pins (horizontal bars) have been positioned just above where the barbell is lowered to at the safe, bottom position of the squat for this trainee. Thus, should he fail on a rep, he would lower the barbell to the safety pins, and escape.

From the bottom left, the sequence for the first rep of a set of squats. The final two photos (bottom right) show the return of the bar to the rack's saddles at the end of the set.

bar.) Then straighten your knees. The bar should move vertically out of the saddles or stands.

Stand still for a few seconds. Check that the bar feels correctly centered. If it feels heavier on one side than the other, put it back on the saddles. If it felt a little unbalanced, reposition the bar, and try again. If, however, it felt considerably lopsided, get out from under the bar, check that you loaded the bar correctly, and make any necessary corrections. Then get under the bar again, position it properly, and unrack it.

Never walk out of squat stands with a bar that doesn't feel properly centered on your upper back.

Step back the minimum distance so that you don't hit the uprights of the rack or squat stands during the ascent. Don't step forward after you've taken the bar out of its supports. If you do, you'll have to walk backward and look to the rear to return the bar to its supports. This is far more hazardous than returning the bar forward to its supports.

Slide your feet over the floor as you walk with the bar. This keeps both of your feet in constant contact with the floor. Put your feet in the stance you've drilled yourself to adopt. Don't look down. At all times while standing with the bar, whether stationary or moving into your stance, maintain a natural degree of lower-back inward curve—keep your chest up and shoulder blades crushed together. Maintenance of the natural strong curves of your spine is critical for back health when bearing weight.

Never look at the ceiling as you squat because that causes severe neck extension, and hinders correct squatting technique. And never look at a spot close to your feet as you squat. Look directly ahead, which means your neck will be extended a little, or, better, fix your eyes on a spot on the floor about two yards (or meters) in front of you—that will help keep your neck in a neutral position (neither extended nor flexed).

The weight should be felt over your entire feet but mostly through your heels, but don't overdo it and rock back on your heels and lose your balance.

Descent

Unlock your knees and sit down and back. The knee and hip breaks should be simultaneous. Maintain a tight back, with your shoulder blades retracted and chest up, and make a deliberate effort to push your chest out and up as you descend, *and* push your hips to the rear. Doing all of this will help to maintain the tight, slightly hollow lower spine—back extension—which is essential for safe, effective squatting.

Descend symmetrically, under control (never drop to the bottom!), with the weight felt over your entire feet but mostly through your heels. If you descend with the weight felt through the balls of your feet, it will stay there on the ascent, and your form will be wrecked. *You must make a correct descent.* Take about three seconds for each one.

Some forward movement of your knees is essential, as is forward lean of your torso. Provided that correct technique is used, how much forward movement and lean occurs depends on your body structure and how deep you squat.

Depth of descent

With poor squatting technique, your lower back will round earlier in the descent than it would had you used correct technique. With correct set-up

Left, a squat to a depth where the tops of the upper thighs are parallel with the floor. The lower spine is still slightly hollow, albeit the hollow is filled with muscle. This is the maximum safe depth for this trainee. Middle, the increased depth has caused his lower back to round. Right, severe rounding or flexion of the lower spine. DANGER. Never allow your back to round in the squat. The right photograph also illustrates the errors of the weight felt mostly over the balls of the feet, and exaggerated forward travel of the knees, whereas the left-most photograph illustrates the weight felt more over the heels. Wrist extension is excessive in all three of these photographs.

and technique, as described here, and just a bare bar, find the depth of descent at which your lower back just starts to round. An assistant must watch you from the side, with his eyes level with your hips at your bottom position.

Set your squatting depth at two inches or five centimeters above the point where your lower back just starts to round. Position the safety bars of the power rack, or squat stands, at that depth.

Ideally, descend until the top of your upper thighs is just below parallel with the floor. *If your lower back starts to round before you reach that position, don't squat that low.* Most trainees who are flexible enough, suited to the barbell squat, and use correct technique, can squat to just below parallel without their lower backs rounding. Don't reduce your squatting depth except for safety reasons.

Although some bodybuilders can squat safely to well below parallel, they are in a minority. You may belong to that minority. If so, rejoice!

Knees coming in on the ascent is a common symptom of set-up flaws in the squat. Insufficient toe flare, and heels too close, are common flaws responsible for buckling of the knees. Tight thigh adductors and weak abductors also contribute.

During the ascent, the bar as seen from the side should move vertically. It mustn't move forward before it moves upward. If you tip forward at the bottom of the squat, the bar will go forward before it starts to go up. This is a common mistake, and has produced many lower-back injuries.

Your hips mustn't rise faster than your shoulders.

Make a special effort to keep your shoulder blades pulled back and your chest pushed out and up as you drive your hips straight up from the bottom position, to help you keep your ascent in the right groove. This means that your back keeps a constant angle as you drive out of the bottom position.

The ascent, like the descent, should be symmetrical. The bar shouldn't tip to one side, and you shouldn't take more weight on one side of your body than the other.

When the hips rise faster than the shoulders, the torso tips forward excessively, and stress is greatly exaggerated on the lower back—danger. Your hips mustn't rise faster than your shoulders.

Ascent

Don't pause at the bottom position. As soon as you complete the smooth, under-control descent, *immediately* start the ascent—smoothly, and then accelerate further. (If you drop somewhat at the bottom of the ascent—typically by relaxing something momentarily—and then blast out of the "hole," you'll increase the perceived weight relative to a controlled descent and a smooth start up.) *Ascend while driving your hips straight upward and keeping your shoulders pulled back.* This should automatically keep the weight mostly over the rear of your feet.

While standing

While standing between reps, don't sway at your hips, don't rock the bar on your shoulders, don't take more of the weight on one foot than the other, and don't rotate your hips. Stay rigid, with the weight distributed symmetrically, and maintain the natural inward curve in your lower spine. If you move your hips forward during the pause between reps, you'll flatten the curve at the bottom of your spine and greatly weaken your back.

Between reps, preserve the natural curves of your spine (left). Don't round your back (right).

Racking the bar

At the end of a set, rack the bar. While sliding your feet so that you always have both of them in contact with the floor, shuffle forward until the bar is directly above the saddles or stands. (If you use racks with vertical uprights, touch the uprights with the bar.) Check that you're not going to miss the bar holders with the barbell, and ensure that your fingers aren't lined up to be trapped between the bar and its holders. Then bend your knees and set the bar down.

The bar should be returned to its holders in a vertical motion. A common error is to stop short of the saddles or stands and lower the bar through leaning forward while keeping the knees straight.

This is dangerous. It leads to reduced control over the bar, and excessive stress on a tired back.

Other tips

Don't squat in a sweaty shirt. Change your shirt before you squat, if need be. Don't squat with a bare torso, because it reduces the stability of the bar on your back.

Before you get under the bar for a work set, put chalk or rosin on your hands, and perhaps get someone to put some on your shirt where the bar will rest. This may help the bar to stay in position.

Increasing shoulder and pectoral flexibility will help you to hold the bar in position with less difficulty.

Practice, practice, and practice, with just a bare bar, until you can get into your correct squatting stance without having to look down or fiddle around to get your feet in the right position.

Never turn your head while you're squatting. If you do, the bar will tip slightly, your groove will be spoiled, and you could hurt yourself.

Don't squat to a bench, box or chair, as that would cause compression of your spine because your vertebrae would get squeezed between the weight up top and the hard surface down below. But you could squat to a soft object of the right height for you, such as a large piece of soft packing foam. When you feel the foam brushing against your buttocks or hamstrings, depending on where the foam is placed, you'll have reached your maximum safe depth without risk of spinal compression.

To help you to improve your squatting technique, record yourself with a video camera from the side view, and analyze the recording.

Once you've mastered the technique, give 100% attention to ensure that you deliver correct technique on every rep. Just a slight slip of concentration can lead to lowering the bar out of position, one hand getting ahead or in front of the other, or one thigh taking more load than the other.

Don't squat if your lower back is sore from an earlier workout, or heavy manual labor. Wait until you've recovered. Furthermore, don't perform any form of deadlift before you squat. Don't fatigue your lower back and reduce its potential as a major stabilizer for the squat.

Don't use a lifting belt. Not only is it not required, a tight belt inhibits 20-rep squatting.

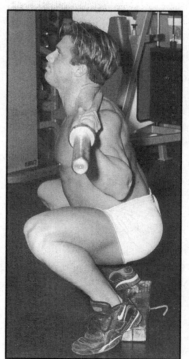

Don't squat with a board, plate or block under your heels. Raising your heels produces a more upright torso, but distorts the balanced spread of stress over the thighs, hips and back. The result is unnecessarily increased knee stress, with potentially harmful consequences.

And don't place the barbell at the base of your neck. The bar position shown here is far too high.

A common single-spotter method of spotting for the squat when just minimal assistance is required. But applying the assistance to the bar—not to the squatter—is a better way to go provided that the assistance is applied evenly and symmetrically.

But neither methods are recommended. Two competent spotters who work in perfect unison at the ends of the barbell is a much better way to proceed.

The best way, however, is to use a power rack, squat racks or a half rack, properly set up, with or without a pair of spotters.

As with the other linchpin exercises, the barbell squat has special breathing requirements for 20-rep work, which are covered elsewhere in this book, including on page 57.

Spotting

The purpose of spotting in general is to take just sufficient of the weight to allow the trainee to complete the rep. It's not supposed to be an intensive effort for the spotter. For the squat, two spotters are required.

As soon as the squat bar stalls, moves laterally, tips, or the squatter starts to twist, the two spotters must act to prevent the rep deteriorating further.

The spotters must have excellent communication and provide synchronized action. If one spotter shouts "Take it!" the other must respond even if the latter thinks the assistance could have been delayed. Assistance must be applied equally to each side, to maintain a horizontal bar.

If there are no spotters, set the bar down immediately (under control) on the safety bars. Don't try to complete a squat unassisted when your technique has started to break down.

Never squat alone unless you use a power rack, squat racks or a half rack, with the safety bars properly positioned for you.

Even if you don't have a pair of spotters—but you *do* use the required safety equipment—your assistant (who counts the reps for you, and encourages you), should be ready to help you

after your final rep. At the end of a hard set of high-rep squats, you'll be exhausted. A pair of guiding hands on the bar from your assistant will help ensure that you get the bar into the weight saddles without any trouble.

A single spotter isn't recommended for the squat because only a little help can be provided, which may not be enough to do the job. And then not only may the squatter be injured, but so may the spotter. The spotter is in a weak position from which to apply assistance, and can easily injure his back.

Use proper safety equipment, for sure. Although that's the minimum, it's sufficient to enable you to squat your heart out safely, and yield great results. If you have two competent spotters standing by, too, so much the better, but the use of the safety equipment precludes spotters being a necessity.

In a top-notch weight room with truly expert spotters, squatting is commonly done outside of a rack. But such a facility isn't typical of most gyms. And that's why the safety equipment option is a necessity for most bodybuilders for most of the time, and why it's so strongly recommended here.

If during any stage of the motion of the barbell squat you feel the weight primarily over the balls of your feet, your technique is wrong. And, worse, if you feel the weight over your toes, especially if your heels come off the floor, your technique is a shambles.

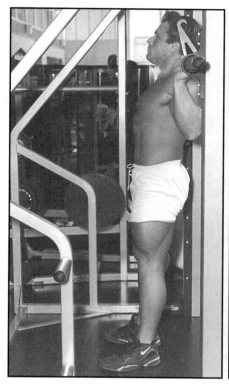

Don't squat in a Smith machine because the rigid, vertical pathway corrupts natural squatting technique. This is hostile to the back and the knees.

The Smith machine squat

The Smith machine squat isn't an alternative to the barbell squat. The alternatives to the barbell squat for **Course #1** are the parallel-grip deadlift, and the hip-belt squat.

Smith machine squats give only an illusion of safety relative to the barbell squat. With the Smith machine, the bar is locked into a fixed pathway so you don't have to be concerned with balance; and you don't have to take a barbell from stands, step back to perform your set, and step forward at the end of a set in order to return the bar to the stands. But when you look further into the Smith machine squat, there are perils.

Don't squat in a Smith machine. Its use is loaded with dangerous compromises. It forces you to follow the bar path dictated by the machine, but the bar path should be dictated by you.

If you put your feet forward, to prevent your knees travelling too far forward at the bottom of the movement relative to your feet, you would put your lower back at risk. If your feet are well forward, you would lose the natural, required slight hollow in your lower spine—including at the bottom of the movement—because your hips would be forward of their ideal position. Although your knees may be spared some stress, it would be at the cost of a back injury, sooner or later.

If you bring your feet back so that they are directly beneath your shoulders, all may look well until you descend. Then your knees would travel forward excessively, the load would shift to over the balls of your feet, the stress on your knees would be exaggerated, and the risk of injury would increase.

Hip-belt squat

Main muscles worked

quadriceps, thigh adductors, buttocks, hamstrings

Capsule description

stand with resistance suspended from your hips and between your legs, hold a support, squat, then stand erect

This squat provides tremendous work for the thighs and buttocks. It permits a deeper squat than can be safely tolerated in the barbell squat because with the hip-belt squat done as follows there's rearward movement of the torso, little or no forward lean of the torso, minimal involvement of the lower back, and reduced forward travel of the knees. Because of the different dynamics of the hip-belt squat and the barbell squat, their technique is different, too.

Set-up and positioning

Find or make two sturdy, broad, non-slip platforms, to stand on. If there's any wobble of the platforms, wedge shims under one or more of the corners. The platforms should be at least 15 inches (38 cms) tall, preferably over 20 (50 cms). The lower the weight hangs from your hips, the more comfortable the set-up may feel, but the more easily the weight will swing. Use a rep speed slow enough to prevent the weight from swinging.

Until you're using about 125 to 150 pounds (57 to 68 kilos), a belt for attaching weight for the parallel bar dip (see page 141) can substitute for a hip belt. But beyond that weight, a heavy-duty hip belt with special attachments is recommended, for comfort and safety. A supplier of such a hip belt is www.ironmind.com.

With a hip belt the weight stack may be attached by straps or chain to the front and rear of the belt, and there may be reduced friction between your body, belt, and attachments compared with other belts. If front and rear attachments are used, the length of the one between the rear of the belt and the loading pin will be longer than that of the front one, maybe by three to four inches. Some trainees may prefer to attach the loading pin to the front of the hip belt only, rather than the front and the rear.

Some trainees may fix the attachments to the hip belt using carabiners (spring clips), but others may fix them directly to the hip belt, and use a carabiner only to make the connection with the loading pin. Multiple carabiners, perhaps of different sizes, could be linked to fine tune the total length of an attachment. If chains are used as attachments, and they are loose near the belt, use an additional carabiner to pull them together.

Safety is paramount. Whatever belt and attachments you use, they mustn't fail you. They must be strong enough to hold the weight. And all carabiners must be heavy duty, and secure. There must be no risk of them opening during a set.

Rest the belt on your hip bones and upper buttocks. Don't cinch it around your waist. Find the most comfortable position for you. Depending on the belt, and the attachments, you may need to use padding such as a folded towel between the belt and your hips, and perhaps between the chains or straps and your body, too.

A heavy-duty set-up for the hip-belt squat.

A loading pin with one 15-kilo and four 20-kilo plates stacked on it, and a 1-1/4 kilo plate between each pair of large plates. The loading pin is attached to a carabiner, which in turn is attached to a hip belt.

A simple, introductory set-up for the hip-belt squat, using a belt designed for applying resistance for the parallel bar dip, and a strong band. The band should be looped around the hands before being grasped in the hands. A slight hollow should be maintained in the lower back at all times. The far right photograph shows some rounding of the lower back—avoid that.

Place the platforms next to a power rack, or a stable, stationary object that's secured to the floor. Space the platforms so that there's just room for a 35-pound or 15-kilo plate on a loading pin to travel up and down without striking the platforms. To accommodate a larger plate you would need to use a wider stance—perhaps too wide. This wouldn't be necessary unless you had a full stack of 35-pounders and needed to use 45-pounders. Another alternative would be continued use of the smaller plates but with a taller loading pin, and taller platforms.

As an alternative to the loading pin, at least to begin with, you could suspend plates or a dumbbell directly from your belt.

You'll be tethered to the rack or other stationary object, so it must be steadfast. If the rack isn't fixed to the floor, load it with sufficient weight on the opposite side to you, so that it can't topple when pulled. Alternatively, have someone pull on the opposite side to you, for counterbalance. There must be no chance of the rack (or other stationary object) moving while you hip-belt squat, or of your feet slipping.

Loop a strong length of towing strap or rope securely around the rack or other stable object, at about the height of your hips when you're standing on the platforms, or lower if the attachment point on the rack is further than about four feet or one meter from the platforms. There must be no risk of the strap snapping, or slipping out of position.

If the strap is fixed on the support at chest height or higher, it will probably lead to your torso leaning forward during the descent.

Strap may be preferable to rope, because the latter may cut into your skin. Alternatively, use rope and wear gloves. You'll need about five meters if you loop the strap around the posts of a rack. The ends of the strap must be within easy reach when you're on the platforms.

Wrap the ends of the strap or rope snugly around your hands next to your thumbs rather than around

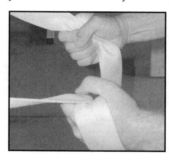

the knuckles at the base of your fingers. Grip the ends securely, so that when you stand on the platforms your elbows are almost straight, and the strap is taut. There must be no chance of losing your grip.

The loading pin should be placed on a sturdy crate or box that's temporarily positioned on the floor between your feet. The pin is loaded while on the crate or box. The loading pin needs to be elevated so that you don't have to squat down far to attach your belt to the loading pin.

Performance

Without a belt or weight, familiarize yourself with the exercise. Stand with the strap around your hands and pulled taut, elbows straight or slightly bent, heels about hip-width, and each foot flared about 30 degrees. Reposition the platforms if need be.

Keep your torso vertical, your neck in a neutral position (neither extended nor flexed), shoulders

The heavy-duty set-up for the hip-belt squat. Regardless of the type of belt used, note the position of the torso with respect to the rack uprights. The torso moves down and back, not merely down.

retracted, and lower spine slightly hollow. As you descend, move your torso and hips to the rear, allow but minimize forward travel of your knees, and keep your back vertical.

If the strap is too short, or the platforms are too far from the rack, you'll lean forward as you descend. If you lean forward, your lower back will round earlier than it would otherwise, which would reduce the safe range of motion for your thighs. Keep your torso vertical. Configure the set-up accordingly.

Take about three seconds for the descent. Descend as low as is safe for your knees and back—ideally to below the point where your upper thighs are parallel with the floor. Then immediately but smoothly ascend to the starting position—push primarily through your heels. Take two to three seconds for each ascent. Straighten your knees at the top, but don't slam into that position.

During each rep, don't tug on the towing strap, or bend your elbows more than just slightly. The purpose of the strap is to enable you to avoid forward lean of your torso, and minimize forward lean of your shins.

Perform several reps, then try slightly different widths of heel spacing, and degrees of toe flare, to find what feels best. And experiment with the length of the strap, to find what works best.

When you're familiar with the exercise, try it with a belt and one plate on the loading pin. Load the pin while it's on the crate. Then grab the towing strap and stand in position on the platforms. Dip the

short distance required to connect the attachment(s) from your belt to the loading pin, using a carabiner. Now, pull your shoulders back, slightly hollow your lower spine, and stand. When the weight is significant, push your hands on your thighs to help you safely into the starting, upright position. Then have an assistant move the crate away. While standing upright on the platforms, loop the strap around your hands until it's taut, and get set for your first rep.

As you descend, the plates should move down and to the rear, as should your hips and torso.

Although there's no compression on your back from the hip-belt squat, still keep your lower spine slightly hollow, for safety. Never round your back, or slump forward. If you can't maintain the right positioning, you may be holding a strap that's too short.

Adjust the length of attachment between your belt and the loading pin so that at your bottom position the resistance is about an inch above the floor, and you're about two inches above the point at which your lower back would start to round.

Get the feedback from an assistant, who should assess you from the side view, to help you to find the right set-up configuration, and to master the performance of the exercise.

Finish each set in the standing, upright position. Then get an assistant to reposition the crate. Set the weight on the crate, release the belt, stand and then rest in order to get ready for any other set.

Don't set the resistance on the floor between reps. If, however, you get stuck on the ascent, descend further than normal, set the weight on the floor, and release the belt. For the next set, reposition the crate under the weight. Strip the loading pin before repositioning it on the crate, and reloading it. But, as much as possible, avoid failing on a rep like this, because releasing the belt is awkward when you're in a full squat, as is getting off the platforms. Both may irritate your knees.

Find the greatest, safe range of motion for you, and then gradually build up the poundage.

Once you know your set-up configuration, be consistent. Always put the platforms the same distance from the rack and same space apart, place the belt around your hips in the same position, use the same attachments between the belt and loading pin, use the same tethering and fasten it to the rack at the same height, grip the strap the same distance from the rack, loop it the same number of times around your hands, and so on.

Especially for men, wear elasticated, giving briefs and shorts (or tracksuit bottoms) while performing the hip-belt squat, or otherwise the tension of the attachments against the clothing around your groin area may produce excessive discomfort.

It may require several workouts of experimentation before you find the hip-belt squat set-up and performance that works best for you. And initially you may find that your lower-back and hip musculature tires quickly once resistance is loaded. Be patient but persistent while you familiarize yourself with the exercise, and adapt to it. The hip-belt squat has the potential to be a safe, highly effective exercise, and especially valuable if you can't safely back squat properly. It's worth the time investment required to master it.

As with the other linchpin exercises, the hip-belt squat has special breathing requirements for 20-rep work—see page 57.

Freestyle hip-belt squat

The hip-belt squat can be done freestyle, without the help of a length of strap or rope. The effect is similar to that of the barbell squat—forward lean, and forward travel of the shins, for example—albeit without a weight bearing down on you.

But the freestyle hip-belt squat doesn't provide the control required by bodybuilders who aren't well suited to the barbell squat. Instead, the freestyle hip-belt squat would yield some of the same problems that the barbell squat does for them.

But bodybuilders who are structurally well suited to the barbell squat will be able to freestyle hip-belt squat well without the assistance of a strap or rope.

With the strap- or rope-assisted hip-belt squat, bodybuilders who don't squat well with a barbell can, by controlling their shin and knee forward travel, and their torso positioning, perform a deep squat that provides safe, effective loading on their thighs and buttocks. It can be a godsend for them.

Tether alternative

Rather than use a strap or rope as a tether, you could configure another non-freestyle set-up. For example, place a barbell across the saddles of a power rack, positioned at the right height for you. Hold the bar as you perform a set. Tinker with the overall set-up until you find what permits the fullest safe range of motion for you.

While this arrangement gives some control over forward lean and forward travel of the shins—to make it superior to the freestyle hip-belt squat—it still doesn't provide the excellent control that the tether-assisted method does. And that's why it's the strap- or rope-assisted method that's most strongly recommended.

Heels and squatting motions

Since you can't lose your balance rearward during the tethered hip-belt squat (provided you don't lose hold of the tether), you can keep almost all the weight over your heels during each rep. This is a big advantage. But with the barbell squat and the parallel-grip deadlift, while you should keep most of the weight over your heels, it's not possible to keep almost all of it there because that would risk loss of balance and serious injury. But with all three exercises, the entirety of your soles and heels must be flat on the floor or platform throughout each set.

Having the weight almost totally over your heels as you go down in the hip-belt squat makes it easy to keep the weight almost totally over your heels as you come up (and push primarily through your heels).

In all three of these knee-flexion exercises, heel emphasis prevents excessive forward travel of the knees, distributes the stress of the exercise well over all the involved musculature, and encourages safety and increased overall effectiveness.

THICK-BAR HOLD

Main muscles worked

finger flexion muscles, forearms

Capsule description

hold a bar next to your thighs while you stand with straight knees

For the best results from timed holds, use a bar that's thicker than usual. A standard bar of an inch, or slightly thicker, will work your grip hard and do a good job, but a thick bar will do a better job. A small increase in diameter produces a substantial change in girth, and a big increase in the difficulty of handling the bar.

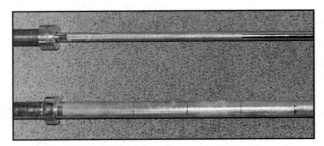

Comparison of a regular-diameter barbell, and a two-inch diameter one.

If there isn't a thick bar where you train, improvise. At the minimum, wrap something around a bar to mimic a thick bar. And use the same modification each time you do the exercise.

Encourage the management of where you train to buy a ready-made thick bar that's knurled. Alternatively, a local metal worker could make one to order. It will be a terrific addition to the gym and won't be expensive unless it's a solid, chromed bar.

Set-up and positioning

Load a bar on boxes, or set it on the pins in a power rack, or across the safety bars in a squat rack, so that you have to pull it up only two inches (five centimeters) or so before holding it in a standing position. Then you'll need to lower it only a little once your grip has given out at the end of the hold. In effect, you hold the lockout position of the deadlift.

Performance

Start with clean, dry hands and bar, and apply chalk or rosin to your fingers, palms, and the inside area of your thumbs and index fingers. Take a pronated grip on the bar a little wider than hip width, and keep the back of each hand in a straight line with its forearm. Then bend your knees a little, pull your shoulders back, hollow your lower spine slightly, and stand upright by simultaneously pulling with your back and straightening your knees.

While standing, keep your knees straight, shoulders retracted, and torso vertical or tilted forward slightly. Never round your back. The bar can be pressed against your thighs, but don't bend your knees or lean backward or otherwise you'll cheat through taking some of the weight on your thighs. Furthermore, leaning backward while supporting a load is harmful for the spine.

During the second half of each timed hold, don't merely grasp the bar. Try to crush it. Just holding the bar isn't the way to get the most staying power out of your grip. Squeeze the bar as hard as possible. Then when your grip is close to failing, try to bend the bar. Although you can't bend it, attempting to can extend the life of your grip. Shrugging your shoulders a little, and keeping your elbows slightly bent, may also help you to get more mileage out of your grip.

Don't be concerned about when to breathe during thick-bar holds—breathe freely. Don't hold your breath.

Select a duration for the holds. Between 30 and 60 seconds will probably suit most trainees. Settle on a specific number of seconds. Once you can hold the bar for that time, add a little weight next session. **Course #1** employs 60-second holds.

In a power rack getting into position for the timed hold, using a thick bar. The pin setting in the rack should be higher than shown here, to make it easier to get the bar into position for the hold.

6

"Some bodybuilders do more training for just two body parts than you're recommending for my entire physique! Is Course #1 for real?"

It's for real all right! The observation you pointed out is one of the major explanations why Course #1 is so effective, and why most other routines are useless for most bodybuilders.

When Peary Rader made his amazing progress, he followed a routine with just four exercises in it. That's proof that the right abbreviated schedule, properly applied, is hugely effective.

The Growth Phase
Course #1's training schedules, and how to apply them

The previous chapters provide essential information. Start on this chapter only after you've studied the first five.

A COMMON CONCERN

Before I get into the training schedules, I want to address the concern you may have that abbreviated training schedules don't have enough volume to build muscle mass.

Remember, Peary had his amazing success from applying a routine of just four exercises. He was a zero gainer for 12 years until he got into that interpretation of **Course #1**. And many other people have made amazing progress on abbreviated training schedules.

Provided that the right exercises are selected, and the routines are implemented as taught in this book, abbreviated schedules *do* have enough exercises and overall volume to build muscle mass. There's no doubt about it!

If you try to build every aspect of your physique in perfect harmony simultaneously, and maintain a high level of definition, you'll never build substantial overall muscle mass. That strategy just doesn't work well for drug-free, genetically typical bodybuilders.

The strategy you require for building substantial muscle mass *necessitates* that you temporarily set aside perfect harmony of development and a high level of definition. You can't have it all while you actually build the muscle mass, but you *can* work on the harmony and definition in between cycles of **Course #1**, so that everything falls into place over time.

You can have mass *and* detail if you go about it properly, as taught in this book.

Have confidence!

A reminder of some compulsory understanding

This book is about how to apply **Course #1**. This routine *requires* hard training and incrementally ever-greater exercise poundages—they are essential elements. (Some other good routines for drug-free, genetically typical bodybuilders don't require such a degree of hard training, or as much focus on ever-greater exercise poundages.)

But excessive training intensity and/or incorrect application of ever-greater exercise poundages will put you at risk of serious injury, and undermine your mental resilience and passion for training.

And even if your training is correct, if you overdo your rate of bodyweight gain, you'll hinder your efforts to improve your physique.

I've painstakingly described the correct application of training intensity, exercise poundage increments, and bodyweight gain, so that you can apply **Course #1** properly, for the best results.

Course #1's schedules are provided in several forms, to accommodate individual variation. One or more of the schedules will work well for you. But implement the schedules as explained in this chapter, *and* incorporate the guidance provided in *The Procedures.*

To build significant muscle during *The Growth Phase,* you must handle ever-greater personal best exercise weights (for the specified reps, in correct form), and go well into new poundage territory.

For an exercise that's new for you, you won't have a previous personal best poundage, but you will the second cycle you use that exercise. You should, however, be sufficiently familiar with at least some of the exercises in your first **Course #1** schedule to be able to know when you're in new poundage territory for those movements. But first time around in a new exercise for you, do the best you can even though you don't have a personal best poundage target to better.

Compound and isolation exercises

There are two basic types of exercises: multi-joint movements, which are commonly called *compound exercises*, and single-joint ones, which are commonly called *isolation exercises.* The barbell squat is a compound exercise because it involves movement at more than one joint, and hence affects a lot of musculature—primarily the thighs, hips and lower back. The leg extension—straightening your knee while seated—is an isolation because it involves movement primarily at only one joint (the knee). It primarily targets the quadriceps (front thighs).

Isolation exercises rarely involve only a single joint, as other joints (and body parts) get recruited to some degree. The *isolation* and *compound* labels are used in this book to differentiate between the two basic groups of exercises but, strictly speaking, they are inaccurate labels.

Compound exercises are often called *big, major,* and *core* movements, whereas isolation exercises are often called *small, little, minor, supplementary, auxiliary,* and *accessory* movements. This is, however, an oversimplification.

What if you're a total beginner?

If you've not yet started lifting weights, or you've been lifting for just a few weeks, follow a full-body routine of about eight exercises (mostly compound ones), for three work sets of 10 reps each, and use correct exercise technique. Do this twice a week for three to four months, increase your poundages gradually over that period, and simultaneously apply *The Foundation Phase* guidance in Chapter 4. Then, once you've fully satisfied the requirements listed in that chapter, you should be ready to implement *The Growth Phase*.

If, during *The Growth Phase*, you feel that your workouts are too short, or not demanding enough in any other way, you're probably not training hard enough to stimulate muscle growth, and thus you wouldn't really be in *The Growth Phase*.

PROGRAM DESIGN

Course #1 has three categories of exercises. This categorization is different to the groups on page 46 for specifying set-rep formats. The first of those groups is the same as the first category below, but the other two groups have selections from the other categories in this section.

1) The linchpin exercises

These are primary compound movements.. There are three of them, but one has two variants.

a) Barbell squat to *just below* the position at which the top of your upper thighs is parallel to the floor, which is what some people refer to as the *full squat*. But to do this safely—with the required slightly hollow lower spine even at the bottom of the motion—requires a body structure that's very well suited to the squat. If you can squat like this, do so, and *rejoice!* It's the ideal. *But if you can't squat like this, shift your attention to the following alternatives.*

b) Barbell squat to the position at which the top of your upper thighs is parallel to the floor (but with the required slightly hollow lower spine even at the bottom of the motion). This requires a body structure that's well suited to the squat. *If you can't squat like this, shift your attention to the remaining two alternatives.* (But even if you can squat to parallel with a slightly hollow lower spine, the parallel-grip deadlift may still suit you better.)

c) Parallel-grip deadlift using as full a range of motion as is safe for you.

d) Hip-belt squat, preferably to just below the position at which the top of your upper thighs is parallel to the floor.

All bodybuilders should be able to hip-belt squat safely and intensively. Because of that, and as noted in *Revelation #11*, alternating the hip-belt squat with the barbell squat *or* the parallel-grip deadlift, from workout to workout, may be a better option for many bodybuilders than doing the barbell squat or the parallel-grip deadlift at every workout.

Don't make the hip-belt squat your exclusive linchpin exercise unless you can't do even one of the other aforementioned possibilities safely and intensively.

Positioning of the linchpin exercise in a workout

One strategy is to open the workout with the 20-rep work (following warming up adequately), when energy is likely to be at its highest. (That's how I always did it.) But some bodybuilders have preferred to do the 20-rep work at the end of a workout, because after giving their all to the linchpin exercise they couldn't do justice to much else. Peary used to do the 20-rep squat last in his workout. The risk in this approach is that you may not be able to train at your best on the linchpin exercise because of your prior efforts on the other exercises.

Initially, do the linchpin exercise first (immediately followed by the breathing pullover or the Rader chest pull), take a break for at least 15 minutes, then resume your workout. If that doesn't work well for you, do the linchpin exercise last (immediately followed by the breathing pullover or the Rader chest pull); but take a break for at least 15 minutes just before you do the linchpin exercise.

2) The complementary exercises

a) barbell bench press *or* dumbbell bench press *or* parallel bar dip

b) chin-up *or* pull-up *or* pulldown *or* row

c) partial deadlift *or* shrug

d) overhead dumbbell press *or* overhead barbell press in front

e) breathing pullover *or* Rader chest pull

Some bodybuilders do a shrug and a variation of the stiff-legged deadlift, to yield six exercises from these five subgroups.

The breathing pullover, or the Rader chest pull, is a mainstay of a **Course #1** schedule and is done right after the linchpin exercise, when your breathing is pronounced. It exaggerates breathing further, to perhaps enhance the overall anabolic effect. It may also help to enlarge your rib cage.

The triceps are heavily involved in the bench press, parallel bar dip and overhead press; the biceps (and other arm flexors) are heavily involved in the chin-up, pull-up, pulldown and row (especially the ones that use a supinated grip); and the forearms are heavily involved in several exercises. This is why isolation work for the arms and forearms is usually not included in **Course #1**.

There's overlap between overhead pressing and some of the other exercises, so the overhead press is sometimes excluded from **Course #1** schedules to minimize exercises. But some bodybuilders choose an overhead press as their single pressing movement. When just one pressing exercise is used in an overall program, the 45-degree incline bench press—also called the 45-degree incline press—is a good choice: midway between the regular bench press and the overhead press. But if you alternate two groups of exercises from workout to workout, you can include an overhead press *and* a bench press or the dip.

3) The optional exercises

a) crunch (regular or reverse), or side bend

b) standing calf raise

c) dumbbell curl or barbell curl

d) thick-bar hold

Depending on the selection of complementary exercises, isolation work for the abs and biceps may be redundant. For example, the chin-up provides major work not just for the lats and some other back musculature, but also the abs, biceps and forearms.

A curl is often included in a **Course #1** schedule because of many bodybuilders' preoccupation with the biceps. Provided the chin-up or the supinated pulldown is included, isolation work for the biceps is redundant on this routine. But if the machine pullover is used instead of the chin-up or the pulldown, for example, the inclusion of a curl would be justified because the pullover doesn't provide any meaningful work for the arm flexors.

The parallel-grip deadlift, partial deadlift, chin-up and pull-up, pulldown, row and shrug place a great demand on the grip, and it's vital that you keep a secure hold of the bar. Although those exercises themselves will strengthen your grip, some low-volume supplementary grip work in the form of the thick-bar hold won't overtrain your forearms or sabotage your overall recovery ability, but will help to strengthen your grip further.

Some of the exercises in the three categories have multiple variations. Chapter 5 explains your options. Choose the exercises most suited to you.

Multiple set-rep formats

Each linchpin exercise requires one work set of 20 reps, but there's a choice of three formats for most of the other exercises, and four format-related training *Options*.

Please review *Procedure #13* (page 46) for a reminder of the details.

Alternating groups of exercises

Rather than repeat the same group of exercises every workout, alternate two different groups. This may yield more balanced musculature, and the variety may also boost your zest for training.

Make the alternate exercises different types of movements. Rather than dumbbell bench press at one workout and barbell bench press at the other, do a single form of the bench press at one workout and the parallel bar dip or the overhead press at the other; and rather than chin-up at one workout and pulldown at the other, chin-up or pulldown at one and row at the other. But unless you're similarly suited to the barbell squat and the parallel-grip deadlift, I don't recommend you alternate them.

Optional intensity boosts

As noted in *Procedure #10*, intensifiers may be helpful when used sparingly:

> But just one or two forced reps, *or* just one negative rep performed as slowly as possible, can be done to finish off just the final set of some exercises no more often than once a week *provided* that the main part of the set was performed correctly in each case. That sparing use of an intensifier may provide a jolt of growth stimulus that helps to sustain progress.

> But for safety reasons, forced reps or other intensifiers shouldn't be performed in the following exercises used in **Course #1**: barbell squat, parallel-grip deadlift, partial deadlift, and side bend. Furthermore, the breathing pullover and the Rader chest pull aren't suited to intensifiers.

The exercises to perhaps apply the intensity boosts to are those that directly work chest, upper back, shoulders, arms and calves. So, on just the final set of those exercises at just one workout on alternate weeks, have an assistant provide just sufficient help so that you can squeeze out one or two forced reps after you've performed every rep possible under your own steam. Or, after you've done your very final rep under your own steam, lower the resistance as slowly as possible—aim for at least 20 seconds for that single negative. On some exercises—for example, the bench press—you would need an assistant to help you return the barbell to the saddles after you've done the negative.

Use a training logbook to keep accurate records of your workouts.

Illustrations of training schedules

There are three groups of schedules for **Course #1**: *Expanded*, *Standard*, and *Abridged*. Each group is listed in multiple variations.

EXPANDED, using the traditional higher-rep format

1. Barbell squat: warm-up plus 1 x 20
2. Breathing pullover: 1 x 20–30
3. Bench press: warm-up plus 3 x 10–12
4. Pulldown: warm-up plus 3 x 10–12
5. Seated back-supported overhead press: warm-up plus 3 x 10–12
6. Partial deadlift: warm-up plus 2 x 10–12
7. Shrug: warm-up plus 3 x 10–12
8. Incline dumbbell curl: warm-up plus 3 x 10–12
9. Standing two-legged calf raise: warm-up plus 3 x 15–20
10. Crunch: 2 x 10–12
11. Thick-bar hold: 60 seconds

EXPANDED, using the lower-rep format

1. Barbell squat: warm-up plus 1 x 20
2. Breathing pullover: 1 x 20–30
3. Bench press: warm-up plus 3 x 6–8
4. Pulldown: warm-up plus 3 x 6–8
5. Seated back-supported overhead press: warm-up plus 3 x 6–8
6. Partial deadlift: warm-up plus 2 x 6–8
7. Shrug: warm-up plus 3 x 6–8
8. Incline dumbbell curl: warm-up plus 3 x 6–8
9. Standing two-legged calf raise: warm-up plus 3 x 10–12
10. Crunch: 2 x 10–12
11. Thick-bar hold: 60 seconds

Especially when training intensity is high, do the partial deadlift just once a week—warm-up plus 2 work sets of 6–8 *or* 10–12. (Perhaps alternate the two formats from week to week.)

The *Expanded* schedules are excessive for most bodybuilders.

Most drug-free, genetically typical bodybuilders wouldn't be able to maintain the required high intensity throughout an *Expanded* schedule or, if they could, they would exceed their recovery abilities unless their training frequency is reduced sufficiently, but perhaps that would prohibit the best volume-frequency balance for the fastest muscle growth.

Better alternatives follow.

When you consider that the breathing pullover or the Rader chest pull, and the thick-bar hold, aren't systemically demanding, the number of very demanding exercises in each schedule is two fewer than the overall number that's listed. The workouts must be abbreviated if they are to be effective. Of course, some of the schedules in this chapter are more abbreviated than others.

But remember . . . performing each workout's linchpin exercise *AS SPECIFIED*—with correct technique, sufficient effort, and enough poundage progression—is *MANDATORY*. Without it, Course #1 doesn't exist.

STANDARD A, using the traditional higher-rep format
1. Barbell squat: warm-up plus 1 x 20
2. Breathing pullover: 1 x 20–30
3. Pulldown: warm-up plus 3 x 10–12
4. Parallel bar dip: warm-up plus 3 x 10–12
5. Partial deadlift: warm-up plus 2 x 10–12
6. Standing two-legged calf raise: warm-up plus 3 x 15–20
7. Crunch: 2 x 10–12
8. Thick-bar hold: 60 seconds

STANDARD A, using the lower-rep format
1. Barbell squat: warm-up plus 1 x 20
2. Breathing pullover: 1 x 20–30
3. Chin-up: warm-up plus 3 x 6–8
4. Parallel bar dip: warm-up plus 3 x 6–8
5. Partial deadlift: warm-up plus 2 x 6–8
6. Standing two-legged calf raise: warm-up plus 3 x 10–12
7. Crunch: 2 x 10–12
8. Thick-bar hold: 60 seconds

STANDARD B, using the traditional higher-rep format
1. Parallel-grip deadlift: warm-up plus 1 x 20
2. Rader chest pull: 1 x 20–30
3. Row: warm-up plus 3 x 10–12
4. Bench press: warm-up plus 3 x 10–12
5. Shrug: warm-up plus 3 x 10–12
6. Standing one-legged calf raise: warm-up plus 3 x 15–20
7. Side bend: warm-up plus 2 x 10–12 each side
8. Thick-bar hold: 60 seconds

STANDARD B, using the lower-rep format
1. Parallel-grip deadlift: warm-up plus 1 x 20
2. Rader chest pull: 1 x 20–30
3. Row: warm-up plus 3 x 6–8
4. Bench press: warm-up plus 3 x 6–8
5. Shrug: warm-up plus 3 x 6–8
6. Standing one-legged calf raise: warm-up plus 3 x 10–12
7. Side bend: warm-up plus 2 x 10–12 each side
8. Thick-bar hold: 60 seconds

STANDARD C, using the traditional higher-rep format

1. Hip-belt squat: warm-up plus 1 x 20
2. Rader chest pull: 1 x 20–30
3. Pulldown: warm-up plus 3 x 10–12
4. Seated back-supported overhead press: warm-up plus 3 x 10–12
5. Partial deadlift: warm-up plus 2 x 10–12
6. Standing two-legged calf raise: warm-up plus 3 x 15–20
7. Reverse crunch: 2 x 10–12
8. Thick-bar hold: 60 seconds

STANDARD C, using the lower-rep format

1. Hip-belt squat: warm-up plus 1 x 20
2. Rader chest pull: 1 x 20–30
3. Chin-up: warm-up plus 3 x 6–8
4. Seated back-supported overhead press: warm-up plus 3 x 6–8
5. Partial deadlift: warm-up plus 2 x 6–8
6. Standing two-legged calf raise: warm-up plus 3 x 10–12
7. Reverse crunch: 2 x 10–12
8. Thick-bar hold: 60 seconds

Note on the chin-up

If you're not currently capable of doing 3 x 6–8 in the chin-up, stick with the pulldown until you've developed the required minimum strength for the chin-up.

Note on the second set of the breathing pullover or the Rader chest pull

A set of breathing pullovers or Rader chest pulls can be performed after the partial deadlift, to yield two such sets in the workout.

Now for illustrations of the type of schedules that Peary used during his amazing growth period—*Abridged*:

ABRIDGED A, using the traditional higher-rep format

1. Barbell squat: warm-up plus 1 x 20
2. Breathing pullover: 1 x 20–30
3. Parallel bar dip: warm-up plus 3 x 10–12
4. Pulldown: warm-up plus 3 x 10–12
The fifth exercise is optional: Thick-bar hold, for 60 seconds

ABRIDGED A, using the lower-rep format

1. Barbell squat: warm-up plus 1 x 20
2. Breathing pullover: 1 x 20–30
3. Parallel bar dip: warm-up plus 3 x 6–8
4. Chin-up: warm-up plus 3 x 6–8
The fifth exercise is optional: Thick-bar hold, for 60 seconds

ABRIDGED B, using the traditional higher-rep format

1. Parallel-grip deadlift: warm-up plus 1 x 20
2. Rader chest pull: 1 x 20–30
3. Bench press: warm-up plus 3 x 10–12
4. Row: warm-up plus 3 x 10–12
The fifth exercise is optional: Thick-bar hold, for 60 seconds

ABRIDGED B, using the lower-rep format

1. Parallel-grip deadlift: warm-up plus 1 x 20
2. Rader chest pull: 1 x 20–30
3. Bench press: warm-up plus 3 x 6–8
4. Row: warm-up plus 3 x 6–8
The fifth exercise is optional: Thick-bar hold, for 60 seconds

ABRIDGED C, using the traditional higher-rep format

1. Hip-belt squat: warm-up plus 1 x 20
2. Rader chest pull: 1 x 20–30
3. Pulldown: warm-up plus 3 x 10–12
4. Incline bench press: warm-up plus 3 x 10–12
The fifth exercise is optional: Thick-bar hold, for 60 seconds

ABRIDGED C, using the lower-rep format

1. Hip-belt squat: warm-up plus 1 x 20
2. Rader chest pull: 1 x 20–30
3. Chin-up: warm-up plus 3 x 6–8
4. Incline bench press: warm-up plus 3 x 6–8
The fifth exercise is optional: Thick-bar hold, for 60 seconds

Which schedules should you use?

Generally, I recommend the *Standard* schedules, but if you consider yourself a very hard gainer, or if you've tried a *Standard* schedule but found it too long or that you needed excessive recovery time between workouts, or if it didn't produce satisfying results for any other reason, use an *Abridged* schedule.

Between cycles of Course #1

Between cycles of **Course #1** you'll use other training schedules. They should include some specific exercises that aren't listed in the schedules for **Course #1**, so that you develop balanced strength and musculature throughout your physique. But don't add additional exercises to the **Course #1** schedules.

Training frequency options

It's vital that you understand your training frequency options. Unless you get the frequency right for you, **Course #1** won't work at its best.

While a few bodybuilders claimed to have prospered from three hard workouts each week on a **Course #1** schedule, most found that frequency excessive, and it limited if not prohibited progress. But some bodybuilders who were successful with three workouts each week didn't train with maximum effort each time. They used a heavy-light-medium format (or heavy-medium-light). Only one workout a week was at maximum intensity—the "heavy" one. The other two used reduced weights, but *for the usual reps*, for "light" and "medium" effort workouts.

Here are three formats of training frequency:

a) *Two full-body workouts every week*, for example Saturday and Wednesday. Perform the same exercises each time, or alternate two schedules of exercises. Either way, one workout could involve some lower-rep sets, and the other could involve some higher-rep sets. But partial deadlift just once a week—at the other workout, substitute the shrug. Each body part will be trained twice a week.

b) *Three full-body workouts every two weeks*, which means training once every fourth or fifth day. For example, work out on Saturday, Wednesday, Monday, Saturday, and so on. Perform the same exercises each time, or alternate two sets of them. Either way, one workout could involve some lower-rep sets, and the other could involve some higher-rep sets. But partial deadlift at alternate workouts, and perhaps substitute the shrug at the other sessions. Each body part will be trained three times every two weeks. Some bodybuilders train on an every-fifth-day format regardless of the varying days of the week that results in, because they prefer a consistent break between workouts.

c) *Two divided workouts every week*, for example Saturday and Wednesday. This format trains most body parts just once a week. Take *one* of the workouts given in the illustrations and divide it into two approximately equal halves—roughly upper-body, and lower-body. Perform half at one workout, and the other half at the other workout. Workouts could have some exercises with lower-rep sets *and* higher-rep sets. For example, consider the *Standard A* workout, and add the shrug:

> ### Day One
> 1. Pulldown: warm-up plus 2 x 6–8 and 1 or 2 x 10–12
> 2. Parallel bar dip: warm-up plus 2 x 6–8 and 1 or 2 x 10–12
> 3. Shrug: warm-up plus 2 x 6–8 and 1 or 2 x 10–12
> 4. Crunch: 2 x 10–12
> 5. Thick-bar hold: 60 seconds
>
> ### Day Two
> 1. Barbell squat: warm-up plus 1 x 20
> 2. Breathing pullover: 1 x 20–30
> 3. Partial deadlift: warm-up plus 2 x 6–8 and 1 x 10–12
> 4. Standing two-legged calf raise: warm-up plus 2 x 10–12 and 1 or 2 x 15–20

For an exercise that has both lower- and higher-rep formats, train hard on all the work sets. Of course, you must use a lesser poundage for the higher reps than for the lower reps, but strive to increase both poundages.

The squat and the partial deadlift are in the same workout so that the lower back is trained just once a week.

While this training frequency format can be very effective for strength gains, it may not be as effective for muscle growth as the other training frequency formats.

There's interplay between length of schedule and frequency of performing it. While two workouts each week of an *Expanded* schedule (page 185) is excessive for most drug-free, genetically typical bodybuilders, if the frequency is reduced to three times every two weeks, that may work for some of them. But, while two workouts each week of an *Expanded* schedule is excessive for most bodybuilders, two workouts each week of a *Standard* schedule (pages 186 and 187) may work, and two workouts each week of an *Abridged* schedule (pages 187 and 188) is even more likely to work.

Problems with training frequency on **Course #1** aren't necessarily with all the exercises. The problem may only be with the barbell squat, the parallel-grip deadlift, and the partial deadlift. The partial deadlift is probably best done at just alternate workouts.

Key point

The 20 reps on the linchpin exercises is the "engine" that drives **Course #1**. And being able to do the 20s *effectively* twice a week is the ideal to strive for—it's what Peary did, for example.

By "effectively," I mean with high intensity, correct exercise technique, an incrementally ever-greater poundage, and muscle growth. But "high intensity" doesn't mean such severity that the required recovery time is excessive—that wouldn't permit an *effective* twice-weekly frequency.

Although the demand on the thighs may be comparable from similarly intensive effort on the hip-belt squat, parallel-grip deadlift and barbell squat, the systemic impact is greater from the latter two exercises, in part because they impose such a heavy demand on the lower back. As a consequence for many bodybuilders, two effective doses of the 20s each week may not be possible from the barbell squat or the parallel-grip deadlift.

That Peary was able to squat effectively twice a week was, in part, due to his favorable leverages for the barbell squat that enabled him, in his own words, to squat "almost vertically." Twice-weekly hard squatting didn't overtrain his lower back. But if he'd had a less favorable structure for the barbell squat, he probably wouldn't have been able to squat hard and effectively twice a week on a sustained basis.

Although you may not be able to barbell squat or parallel-grip deadlift *effectively* twice a week, you may be able to three times every two weeks, but that wouldn't yield two doses of the 20s each week.

And this is why, for many bodybuilders, the ideal may be to alternate between the barbell squat or the parallel-grip deadlift at one workout, and the hip-belt squat at the other. Then, on a twice-weekly training frequency, you may have a good chance of getting two *effective* doses of the 20s each week provided that you recuperate quickly enough from each workout. But this may require that you use an *Abridged* schedule rather than a *Standard* one.

Individual variation—in genetics, age and recovery ability, for example—can be considerable, and as a result there's no one-size-fits-all approach to Course #1, or any other routine.

Scheduling recommendations

Start by alternating two different *Standard* schedules on a twice-weekly frequency. Use the traditional higher-rep format at each workout for the respective exercises (*Option A*, page 46), or, perhaps better, alternate that format workout to workout with the lower-rep format (*Option C*, page 47), as in the following illustration. (But if you consider yourself a very hard gainer, use *Abridged* schedules right from the start, like Peary did.)

STANDARD schedule using the traditional higher-rep format

1. Barbell squat *or* parallel-grip deadlift: warm-up plus 1 x 20
2. Breathing pullover: 1 x 20–30
3. Pulldown: warm-up plus 3 x 10–12
4. Parallel bar dip *or* bench press: warm-up plus 3 x 10–12
5. Partial deadlift: warm-up plus 2 x 6–8
6. Standing one-legged calf raise: warm-up plus 3 x 15–20
7. Crunch: 2 x 10–12
8. Thick-bar hold: 60 seconds
   Breathing pullovers or Rader chest pulls can also be performed after the partial deadlift.

STANDARD schedule using the lower-rep format

1. Hip-belt squat: warm-up plus 1 x 20
2. Rader chest pull: 1 x 20–30
3. Row: warm-up plus 3 x 6–8
4. Seated back-supported overhead press: warm-up plus 3 x 6–8
5. Shrug: warm-up plus 3 x 10–12
6. Standing two-legged calf raise: warm-up plus 3 x 10–12
7. Side bend: warm-up plus 2 x 10–12 each side
8. Thick-bar hold: 60 seconds

Only if you can't barbell squat or parallel-grip deadlift safely and intensively should you employ the hip-belt squat at both workouts.

Possible adjustments

a) If you can't progress well into new exercise poundage territory on the *Standard* schedules despite fully satisfying the components of recuperation every day, make both of your weekly workouts *Abridged* schedules.

b) Test that adjustment for at least a few weeks, to see whether or not you can resume exercise poundage progression. If it's unsuccessful, apply the *Abridged* schedules to *training frequency format (b)* for more recovery time (see page 189). Assuming that you can barbell squat or parallel-grip deadlift safely and hard, you may be able to perform that linchpin exercise at each workout on this reduced frequency, and make progress; but you may still be better off alternating the hip-belt squat with the barbell squat *or* parallel-grip deadlift.

c) Test that adjustment for a few weeks, to see whether or not you can resume poundage progression. If it's unsuccessful, apply *training frequency format (c)* to a *Standard* schedule.

But what may work well for the first two months of *The Growth Phase*—as an example—may not for the next two months. As soon as your progress starts to dry up, be sure that your recuperation really is in perfect order, and that you really are training hard, and then try one or more of the recommended adjustments, to restore progress.

Learn what's best for you.

Then, during your next cycle of **Course #1**, you may want to experiment with another *Option*. See *Procedure #13* (pages 46 and 47).

The briefest versions of **Course #1**

A few bodybuilders may need an even more abbreviated version than the *Abridged* one in order to make good or perhaps amazing progress. If you fall into this category, apply the super-abbreviated version—just *two* exercises in a single workout—or the most-abbreviated version, which has just *one* exercise in a single workout.

Peary was the grand doyen of abbreviated training, and he reported the success that some men had from following the simplest of schedules. He noted that "many" great strongmen had spent "long periods" on just a single exercise—"the barbell squat"—and made "amazing" gains in strength and muscle development. This was before bodybuilding drugs were available.

For bodybuilders not well suited to the barbell squat, the prime candidate for a single-exercise workout is the parallel-grip deadlift. And perhaps Peary would have agreed, had the parallel-grip deadlift bar been readily available during his era.

As an illustration of a two-exercise version of **Course #1**, on one day each week do the 20-rep barbell squat *or* parallel-grip deadlift along with the chin-up *or* pulldown, and on another day each week do the hip-belt squat along with the parallel-bar dip *or* a bench press.

For a one-exercise version, perform the 20-rep barbell squat *or* parallel-grip deadlift twice a week, or, probably better, do that exercise just once a week and use the hip-belt squat on another day each week.

Because of the minimal training volume, you may be able to train with better results on a twice-weekly frequency than you could even on an *Abridged* schedule. The even greater reduction in training volume can make a significant difference in your ability to recuperate and grow. But for both the two- and the one-exercise options—especially if you're a very hard gainer—if you need an additional day or two of rest between workouts to fully recover, take it.

Of course, you must give your all to the extremely limited training. (But it's easier to train hard on a reduced volume of work.) Then, provided you fully satisfy the components of recuperation every day, you should grow.

Never mind if you're the only person where you train who uses very abbreviated schedules. So what if you temporarily have to turn to a super-radical method in order to make good progress? Don't feel self-conscious.

Results are what matter, not just clocking up time in a gym. But once your results are clearly visible, you'll be a beacon for **Course #1**.

A real-life illustration

The first time I tried to apply a version of **Course #1** was when I was about 17. I used a schedule similar to those in the *Expanded* group. I was super dedicated (fanatical, actually). I trained hard, ate a great deal, slept generously, and my recuperative powers were high. I briefly tried to train three times a week, but that was impossible to sustain—I had far too little recovery time. So I stuck to twice a week, and the same full-body schedule each time.

I trained on Sundays and Wednesdays. The Sunday workouts were the better ones—probably because Wednesday to Sunday gave me four days of recovery, whereas Sunday to Wednesday gave me just three. Had I trained that particular schedule three times every two weeks, my recovery would probably have been complete from each workout. But, better, had I used an *Abridged* schedule, I believe I would have recovered fully from each of two workouts per week.

My application had other problems, also due to my ignorance at the time. I didn't know what correct exercise technique was (and I often got injured), I didn't realize that I wasn't well suited to the barbell squat, I didn't know about the parallel-grip deadlift and the hip-belt squat, I didn't know about small weight plates and the importance of very gradual poundage progression, and I didn't know much about the interplay of length of schedule and frequency of training. My progress was very limited because of those factors. And because I consumed too many calories—lots of solid food *and* a gallon of milk a day during some periods—a lot of what I gained was body fat.

A couple of years later I tried a more abbreviated interpretation, with better results, albeit nothing like they could have been had I really known what to do at the time.

In my early youth I didn't apply **Course #1** *properly.*

I returned to the routine in my late-twenties. I used it for a few cycles during the following several years, with success. The final time was for the longest duration I ever applied a version of **Course #1**. My recovery ability was severely hampered then because of the demands from family and work. My two daughters were very young at the time, and I was busy with *HARDGAINER* magazine while still working as a school teacher. I was working 80+ hours a week, and my sleep was impaired in both quantity and quality. To try to compensate, I applied *training frequency format (c)* to a schedule akin to a *Standard* one—see page 189 for an illustration (but I had just three or four exercises in each workout). It was at the end of that cycle that I deadlifted 400 pounds (182 kilos) for 20 reps, as I chronicled in Chapter 17 of *BEYOND BRAWN*.

With hindsight, I believe that my best muscle-building progress would most likely have resulted from training twice a week, alternating two *Abridged* schedules—the same basic format Peary applied, albeit he used the same schedule each workout. Both of my schedules would have been different to his. At one workout each week I should have done this: parallel-grip deadlift, Rader chest pull, incline bench press, and a chest-supported row. At the other workout I should have done this: hip-belt squat, breathing pullover, parallel bar dip, and chin-up. But I would have had to fully satisfy all the components of recuperation each day—my recovery ability would have had to be *perfect*. That package of training and recuperation is what I wish I had dedicated myself to during my youth for one cycle every 12 months or so, for several consecutive years.

In between cycles on **Course #1** I should have shifted my attention away from fast overall muscle growth. Instead, I should have trimmed any excess body fat, and applied other premier routines, so that I developed a lean, proportionate physique, with balanced strength throughout.

Other bodybuilders are different, of course—in genetics, the exercises that suit them best, how hard they train, how well they recover, how near they are to realizing their potential, and so on—but my experiences and with-hindsight thinking may help you to work out what's best for you.

Poundage progression

Make incrementally ever-larger exercise poundages a vital part of your training, but be a model for correct exercise technique, and consistency with rep speed, range of motion, and inter-rep and inter-set rest intervals, according to a given exercise and set-rep format.

When you're training very hard and in new exercise poundage territory (or very close to entering it), here are the guidelines for poundage progression:

a) For a linchpin exercise, provided you complete your 20 reps unassisted, in correct exercise technique, and with just two reps to spare—you could squeeze out 22 if your life depended on it, although you stop at 20—add a tad of weight next time. If you don't have the two reps to spare, wait a workout or two until you do, then add a tad of weight. (But if completing the 20 reps is a crushing *death march*, reduce the poundage a little, then gradually rebuild it.)

b) For a traditional higher-rep format exercise, provided you can do 12 reps on the first set (or 20 reps for your calves), unassisted and in correct exercise technique, increase the poundage a tad next workout you use that exercise and format. Because the inter-set rest period isn't short, use the same weight for all the work sets for a given exercise. Your reps may slip a little from set to set, but that's acceptable. Do your best to keep the reps up. But it's still the first set of this format that's the priority one for record keeping and progress monitoring.

c) For a lower-rep format exercise, when you can do all three sets for at least six reps each (or at least ten reps for your calves), unassisted and in correct exercise technique—for example, eight-seven-six or eight-six-six—increase the poundage by a tad next workout you use that exercise and format.

d) For a non-traditional higher-rep format exercise, provided you can do 12 reps on the first set (or 20 reps for your calves), unassisted and in correct exercise technique, increase the poundage a tad next workout you use that exercise and format. Because the inter-set rest period is short, and the weight is decreased for each subsequent set to keep the reps up, it's not possible to regulate the reps precisely for each set beyond the first one. Do your best to adjust the weight between sets so that you can just squeeze out the required 10 to 12 reps each time (or 15 to 20 reps for your calves), but if you slip a little under, that's fine. (After a few workouts you'll get to know how much to reduce the weight on a particular exercise in order to keep the reps where you want them.) It's the first set of this format that's the priority one for record keeping and progress monitoring.

e) For the breathing pullover and the Rader chest pull, there's no progression in poundage. Instead, increase your depth of breathing, and degree of rib-cage expansion.

f) For the timed hold, provided you complete the 60 seconds unassisted, in correct exercise technique, and with five seconds to spare—you could do the additional seconds if your life depended on it—add a tad of weight next time.

g) For the remaining exercises—namely, the crunch and the side bend—when you've done both sets of 10 or more reps, unassisted and in correct exercise technique (for example, 12-11, or 12-10, or 11-10), increase the poundage by a tad next time.

Review *Procedures 14, 15, 16 and 17* (pages 48+) for the essentials on how to make relentless progression a reality. And specifically recall this extract concerning the ideal rate of progress:

> You don't need the little gems during the first part of a cycle when you're not using your current best poundages. But once you've built back to just a few pounds short of your current best weights—and you're close to going into new exercise poundage

territory and *The Growth Phase*—get out your little gems and *nudge* up your weights as often as possible (ideally, every week).

Then this week's 256 pounds for 20 reps in the barbell squat or parallel-grip deadlift, for example, should feel no more difficult than last week's 254; and then next week's 258 should feel no more difficult than this week's 256, and so on. Later on, perhaps drop to just a one-pound increment per week. **Course #1**, properly applied, produces *relentless progression*, and *gaining momentum*—it's the "slow cooking" way to progress, for month after month after month.

How much the increment will be during *The Growth Phase* depends on the particular exercise, how well you apply **Course #1** and the related factors, your potential for muscle and strength, and how near you are to reaching that potential. It could be two pounds or one kilo in the squat or the parallel-grip deadlift each week, and half of that in the bench press or the parallel bar dip, for example. And the increment could be halved for the final stage of a cycle.

Keep accurate records of your workouts.

Proper progression in the 20-rep work

For 20-rep work to be effective, it must be implemented properly. Discard the approach that advises this: "Take a weight you can squat only 10 reps with, then force yourself to get 20, and add five pounds every workout!" Of course, if you could do 20 reps with a certain weight, it wasn't really a 10-rep weight.

The idea is not to almost die in the effort to get all 20 reps or, worse, not get all 20 despite such a huge effort. Make progress in poundage slowly but steadily, rather than try to pack all the progress into just a few weeks but burn out after just a couple, and perhaps sustain an injury.

At the end of *The Foundation Phase* you reached weights for the hip-belt squat and the barbell squat or the parallel-grip deadlift with which you could comfortably get 20 reps and have enough slack to be able to grind out 30 reps if you really had to. Now, add five pounds or two-and-a-half kilos per week until you're *almost* at the point where could do no more than just two reps in excess of the 20 if your life depended on it, but you stop at 20. Then start the "slow cooking" method of progression. Although this approach is very demanding, it will never crush you, and you can keep it going for month after month after month.

If, when you've done a set of "20 reps with just two to spare," you thought it wasn't very demanding, your assessment of the 22-rep weight was inaccurate. A true "20 reps with just two to spare" set *is* very demanding, but not quite a death march.

A set of intensive 20-rep squats or parallel-grip deadlifts is a workout in itself—a test of body and spirit. But you must take your time to adapt to the demands involved. The demands aren't just muscular. Your heart and lungs need to adapt, as does your entire supporting structure including your shoulder girdle, vertebral column, and feet.

While intensive 20-rep hip-belt squats are very demanding, they aren't quite as severe as intensive 20-rep barbell squats or parallel-grip deadlifts. But, for best results, they still need to be worked into gradually, and *The Growth Phase* carried out just like with the other linchpin exercises.

If you proceed as recommended, you'll shortly be able to train with an intensity that may shock you when compared with how you usually train, but if you try to jump immediately to that level of effort, you're unlikely to be able to maintain it for long enough to stimulate substantial growth.

Forced breathing

Remember that the benefits from the barbell squat, the parallel-grip deadlift and the hip-belt squat don't come just from the localized muscular work. Provided these exercises are trained hard for high reps, with accompanying heavy, forced breathing, and progressively ever-heavier poundages over time, there's an anabolic effect that boosts overall growth. There may even be a testosterone surge from each bout of it.

Remember this general guide from *Procedure #23*, on breathing and 20-rep work:

> Pause sufficiently to take one or two deep breaths before each of reps 1 to 5, two or three deep breaths before each of reps 6 to 10, four or five before each of reps 11 to 15, and six to eight before each of reps 16 to 20. Breathe through your mouth as deeply as possible and fill your chest (not merely expand your abdomen).

> Once you've taken your final super-duper deep breath before a rep of a linchpin exercise, *hold* it and immediately perform the next rep. The tradition for 20-rep work is to hold the final breath during both the descent *and* the ascent of the next rep. Provided you work into the 20-rep work gradually, as this book instructs, you should adapt to the breath holding and not suffer any lightheadedness or headaches. But if you do suffer lightheadedness or headaches despite your best efforts to adapt, exhale during the ascent rather than immediately after it.

> Aside from breath holding, the sheer volume of breathing during 20-rep work can cause lightheadedness if you don't work into it gradually.

In the barbell squat, keep the bar over your upper back throughout each set, stand upright between reps, hold your body safely and securely, without rounding your back, without losing or exaggerating the natural arch in your lower spine, and without swaying at your hips.

With the parallel-grip deadlift, if you pause between reps as you stand while holding the bar, your grip will fail before you've adequately worked your major muscular structures, and your freedom to breathe deeply will be compromised. Instead, set the bar on the floor and briefly stand between reps while you take your deep breaths. Alternatively, pause while the weight is on the floor, your hands still on the bar but relaxed, and your knees straight; then take your deep breaths, immediately squat down and get into position to perform the next rep, do the rep, and so on. You may find the effect on your chest from the breathing to be greater with the latter method.

With the hip-belt squat, there should be no problem with your grip, and the weight doesn't bear down on you. The between-reps forced breathing (while standing upright) is much easier to do with this exercise than the other linchpin movements.

Rep counting, and breath counting

During a 20-rep work set, count just the breaths between reps. Your training partner or other assistant should count the reps aloud. If you try to count breaths *and* reps you'll probably lose track of the reps. If you train alone, count just the reps, but take plenty of breaths between reps although you don't actually count the breaths. It's more important that you're accurate with your rep count than your breath count.

It doesn't matter if you don't make the precise number of breaths before a certain rep. So long as you're close, that's fine. But breathe a lot, and very heavily. If in doubt, take the extra breaths rather than rush and take too few. With experience, you'll find your own rhythm of breathing, and increase in breath count as the set proceeds. Correct exercise technique, training hard, getting the full 20 reps, and relentless albeit gradual poundage progression are the absolute priorities, along with lots of heavy, forced breathing.

Even if you don't have a training partner, *still* get someone to count the reps for you—recruit someone who's in the gym at the time. It's tremendous help to have someone count your reps, and encourage you, too.

"Breathing squats"

High-rep squatting with maximum poundage for the selected reps is one form of "breathing squats," because the heavy breathing that's naturally produced is exaggerated. The breaths are done with an exaggerated depth, and more breaths are done than are necessarily required. But the primary concern of the exercise is getting all the target reps—most traditionally 20—and gradually increasing that weight as the weeks and months go by. The exaggerated breathing is secondary, albeit still important. This is the form used in **Course #1**. And the "breathing squat" can be barbell or hip-belt style, and a key variation for many bodybuilders is the "breathing parallel-grip deadlift."

Another form of the "breathing squat" is the one promoted by Roger Eells in the 1930s. The emphasis is on the breathing, not the weight. No more than the bodyweight of the individual concerned is used for the barbell squat—and much less weight in many cases, depending on the strength of the individual.

In both forms, breathing is done through the mouth, to maximize inhalation.

In the first form of the "breathing squat," the demands of the squatting automatically produce heavy breathing, but not so in the Eells-style. Instead, the deep breaths between reps are forced right from the start of the set. Whereas 20 reps is the usual number for the maximum-poundage style, 20 is the minimum in the other style, with 30 being "preferable" in Eells' description, and as many as 40 reps being better still. Three or more deep breaths while standing between reps were advised, and as many as eight to ten breaths. Each breath must be sufficient to raise the chest and make the squat bar rise.

Both styles have had their advocates, with supporters of each claiming impressive results. In both cases, the squats are done in the context of an abbreviated training routine, and a ribcage stretching exercise is supersetted with the squats to further emphasize breathing and perhaps produce ribcage enlargement. And recuperation must be generously attended to in both cases.

Eells' premise was that his method of specializing on the chest through an effort to expand it not only enlarges the chest but stimulates the metabolism and promotes growth throughout the body. It was sometimes recommended as a last resort for ultra hard gainers, even those who had followed the maximum-effort, heavier format without success.

But, probably, those who didn't have success with the heavier format didn't apply it properly. They didn't use a sufficiently abbreviated schedule, or they didn't train hard enough on it, or they didn't sufficiently attend to the components of recuperation, or they didn't stick with it long enough or for enough cycles. Or, most likely, there were deficiencies in all of these areas.

Generally, the heavier format is the better of the two for overall bodybuilding purposes, and that's why it's the one used for **Course #1**. It was the style promoted by Peary Rader, but he stressed the importance of combining it with heavy, forced breathing.

How to perform a 20-rep set of a linchpin exercise

Never forget that properly performed 20-rep work on a linchpin exercise is the "engine" that drives **Course #1**. Without that "engine" you wouldn't have **Course #1**.

By "properly performed 20-rep work" I mean intensive training using correct exercise technique, with a gradually ever-greater poundage, and eventually using an impressive weight.

Once you reach *The Growth Phase*, each 20-rep set is a workout in itself. And if those sets aren't the hardest you've ever done, you probably haven't done them as required, and thus won't get the results you want.

During *The Growth Phase* you'll probably think a lot about the 20-rep sets even when you're out of the gym. I used to get the jitters, and had trouble getting to sleep at night if I got thinking about the 20s—particularly reps 16 through 20.

Think about the 20s *positively*. Never contemplate failure. You must get all 20 reps on every occasion—in your imagination, and in reality. Shortly before a set of 20s, mentally rehearse a perfect set. Then go and grind out a perfect set in reality.

Here's a template for such a set, whether it's of the barbell squat, the parallel-grip deadlift, or the hip-belt squat. Apply it (or something very close to it), and you should do very well indeed.

Cast your eyes around the location for the 20s. Look at the nearby walls and some of the blemishes, photographs and whatever else may be on them. Look at the equipment you're going to use for the 20s, then put a hand on it. Feel at one with it. Shift into your training persona.

Do your warm-up sets. Get ready for the work set. Enter your *training sanctuary.*

Have your training partner or alternative assistant stand by to count the reps out loud for you, and to encourage, cajole and badger you to get all 20 reps. With experience you'll learn whether you respond best to aggressive pep talks, or a low-key approach.

Check your training log for the required poundage. Load the barbell, shrug bar, or hip-belt squat loading pin. Get in position for the first rep.

Take two deep breaths through your mouth; fill your chest with air each time. Immediately after the second breath, do your first rep (in correct technique, of course). Hear "One!" ring out.

Repeat this process for the next four reps, and hear the rep count ring out after each one. The reps aren't difficult to perform, yet, but they still require your total focus in order to get the technique right. Be consumed by the performance of the individual reps. Nothing else matters.

Rep #6 now. Take three deep breaths through your mouth; fill your chest each time. Immediately after the final breath, do your sixth rep (again, in correct technique). Hear "Six!" ring out.

Repeat this process for the next four reps, and hear the rep count ring out after each one. Although the reps still aren't difficult to perform, they are less comfortable than the first five, and require your total focus in order to get the technique right. Be consumed by the performance of the individual reps. Nothing else matters. Be the master of the set.

Rep #11 now. Take five deep breaths through your mouth; fill your chest with air each time. Immediately after the final breath, do your eleventh rep (once again, in correct technique). Hear "Eleven!" ring out.

Repeat this process for the next four reps, and hear the rep count ring out after each one. Each rep is incrementally more demanding to perform, but you're the master of each one.

"Twelve!"

"Thirteen!"

"Fourteen!"

"Fifteen!"

Rep #16 now, and the start of the *battle royal*—the final five reps. Your mind must control your body, and keep the reps happening. Take six or more deep breaths through your mouth; fill your chest with air each time. Immediately after the final breath, do your sixteenth rep (yet again, in correct technique). Hear "Sixteen!" ring out.

As the discomfort intensifies, dissociate yourself from it. Imagine you're watching yourself on film. Take it just one rep at a time. Hear your training partner or assistant encouraging you. Feel your mastery of the set. *Deliver training ferocity.* Nothing else matters.

"Seventeen!"

The final few reps are the "growth reps." The others were mere preparation. Only if you perform the final few reps will you earn victory, and progress. But nothing will deny you victory.

Again, dissociate yourself from the discomfort. *Push on!*

"Eighteen!"

Your training partner, or assistant, shouts out a vivid life-or-death situation where, if you fail to make the rep, you'll die. *Then make the rep.*

"Nineteen!"

Just one to go. Yet again, dissociate yourself from the discomfort. *Push on!*

Your training partner, or assistant, shouts out another vivid life-or-death situation where, if you fail to make the rep, you'll die. *Then make the rep.*

"Twenty! You're done."

Drag yourself over to a nearby bench for the breathing pullover, or to what you hold onto for the Rader chest pull; then as you do your pullovers or chest pulls, wallow in the satisfaction from the completion of a terrific set of 20s.

Initially, you may be apprehensive about the 20s. But once you get the hang of them, become better able to tolerate exercise-induced discomfort, and just *nudge* up your exercise poundage (each workout, ideally), you'll revel in the satisfaction you get from the linchpin work. And you'll love the results it yields.

Make your 20-rep sets heroic efforts!

More on the intensity of the 20-rep work

The time-honored tradition of 20-rep work is that it's done with high intensity (other than during the introductory part of a cycle). There's no tradition of multiple work sets of a lesser intensity.

During all my stints of 20-rep squatting I applied the death-march method (other than during the first part of each cycle when I worked up to my current best poundage from a moderate starting weight—which, in my ignorance, I usually rushed). I believed that if hard training on the 20s was good, even harder training must be better, and death-march training must be best. The twentieth rep in each work set was usually a do-or-die effort. And provided I got all 20 reps, the following workout I tried to do the same again but with an additional five pounds on the bar. But those sets limited my progress. I couldn't maintain the too-fast rate of progress for long, I sometimes failed to get all 20 reps despite colossal effort, and I often got injured. (Had I inherited better leverages for the squat, like Peary had, perhaps I wouldn't have sustained so many injuries.)

Although I eventually made substantial progress largely because of 20-rep routines, I made many mistakes along the way. Had I applied **Course #1** *as it's taught in this book, I would have made greater progress, and without the problems that blighted my actual efforts.*

Don't train the 20s death-march style. For all the linchpin exercises, make 22 reps the death-march number (if you were to go to your absolute limit), but stop at 20. That's the intensity I recommend, but it's still sufficiently demanding to require heroic effort. Then provided you *nudge* up your poundage, that very demanding but not death-march intensity should yield at least three to four consecutive months of steady progress.

There's a risk, however, in recommending less than 100% effort in the 20s. Imagine someone who *thinks* he trains at death-march level although he could actually do several additional reps if he was properly supervised and motivated. If he applies the "20 reps with just two to spare" recommendation, he may not train hard enough to stimulate any muscle growth. What he thinks is a death-march 22-rep number is no such thing, and the last thing he needs is to hold back further. He needs to *crank up* his intensity. Be honest when you assess your own training intensity.

Most bodybuilders don't train hard enough even though many of them think that they train hard. And very few bodybuilders overdo training intensity.

But even the recommended level of effort for the 20s is so demanding that it's by far the most arduous part of **Course #1**. Absolute-maximum-intensity sets in the other major exercises in the routine are less arduous than the "20 reps with just two to spare" in a linchpin exercise. But if you find otherwise, then what you interpreted as "20 reps with just two to spare" was really more like "20 reps with five to spare," which is insufficiently demanding for *The Growth Phase*.

Unless the "20 reps with just two to spare" is the toughest training you've probably ever done, chances are that you haven't done it hard enough.

Of course, the bottom line isn't training intensity per se, but *progress*. Provided you go into new poundage territory and your muscles are growing, albeit slowly, whatever training intensity you're delivering is working. Some trial and error may be necessary in order to discover what intensity works best for you, but, generally speaking, it's much more likely that you'll need to train harder, than easier. It's usually only the death-marchers who may be better off if they ease back a little.

But, if you're super-motivated, use a linchpin exercise and training frequency that are well suited to you, apply correct exercise technique consistently, fully satisfy the components of recuperation, and just *nudge* up your exercise poundage, the death-march approach will be very effective, but such severe intensity isn't essential. A little less intensity may be as effective, if not more so.

Peary Rader's own training, and advice

Here's a summary of Peary's training during his famous period of amazing growth, and the advice he provided on **Course #1** through his *Master Bodybuilding and Weight Gaining System*, and his articles in *Iron Man*.

He trained twice a week. The only exercises he did were the barbell squat, breathing pullover, chin-up and press behind neck. (Peary didn't learn about the Rader chest pull until later, and that's why he used the breathing pullover initially.) He followed what I've termed the *Abridged* interpretation of **Course #1**. (I don't recommend the press behind neck. The barbell press in front, or the dumbbell press, would be a better choice.) Peary later wrote that, with hindsight, he would revise that routine to the squat, breathing pullover or Rader chest pull, bench press and bent-over row.

He noted that when he was on his version of **Course #1**, in the early 1930s, it was the norm to do just one work set per exercise. He did his squats rest-pause fashion, with heavy, forced breathing between reps, as I've already explained. Peary noted that he worked so hard that he couldn't do another set of the squat even if he had wanted to. He said that it took five to ten minutes after completing the squats before his breathing returned anywhere near to normal, and before he was able to stand up and walk. Clearly, Peary had the mental fortitude required to drive a protesting body on to complete all 20 reps.

He performed the squat last in his routine (followed by the breathing pullover). And he squatted with his feet "well apart," and his toes "pointed well outward," and had the leverages that enabled him to squat "almost vertically." He preferred a cambered bar to a straight one.

He explained that, if he got stuck at the bottom, he would take one hand off the bar and use it to push against a thigh to enable him to get up. *But don't do that yourself—use spotters, a safety set-up with spotter bars properly in place, or (best of all) spotters AND that safety set-up.*

Peary's descriptions of the 20-rep squats he did during his amazing growth period indicate that he trained at least close to death-march level. But that he did it twice a week suggests that the intensity, albeit high, wasn't at a level that crushed him and required excessive recovery time.

He noted that at the start of the 20-rep routine he used "about" 135 pounds, and gradually built up to 20 with 340 pounds. But here's where there's confusion. In the 1967 *Iron Man* article that specifies those poundages, Peary noted that the routine lasted "a year or so." That's at odds with the 25 months specified in his 1956 *Master Bodybuilding and Weight Gaining System* and some *Iron Man* articles in the 1950s. Based on the 25 months duration (which is more likely to be the accurate one), the 200 pounds progress on the squat works out at an average of 8 pounds a month, or about 2 pounds a week, which is about a single pound per workout. The "a year or so" duration would double that rate of poundage gain—to about 2 pounds per workout.

Peary reported that he tried to increase his squat poundage by 5 or 10 pounds at each workout. He said that although it seemed that he couldn't make it, he "always did." But these numbers don't square with what actually occurred over the duration of the training cycle, and this may be from where the urging by some people to increase the squat poundage at an unrealistic rate originated. (Of course, if you start with a very comfortable poundage, you can increase at this faster rate just to begin with, but once the sets become somewhat of a challenge to complete, slow the rate of progression to what's manageable.)

Even if we take the lower end of Peary's target poundage increase—5 pounds at each workout—that would translate to 10 pounds a week, because he trained twice a week. If we take the "a year or so" time frame, that would mean about 50 x 10, or 500 pounds; and if we take the 25 months time frame, that would mean over 1,000 pounds. But his actual total poundage increase was about 200 pounds. *Clearly, Peary's actual rate of progress was way slower than the "5 or 10 pounds each workout" that he tried to achieve.*

But in a 1961 *Iron Man* article, Peary wrote that 1.25-pound plates were "handy" for 20-rep squats; and he also used to have half-pound plates "that worked well." So, Peary was aware of the value of little gems, and a conservative approach to poundage progression.

He stressed that even hard work on an excellent training routine must be combined with sufficient food, sleep and rest in general, in order to yield progress.

In a 1955 *Iron Man* article Peary noted that during his period of amazing growth he didn't use the 20-rep squat throughout the two years or so (but he did stay with the *Abridged* schedule.) A steady diet of 20s was too much for such a sustained period, even for a man with extraordinary motivation and dedication. He noted that he used the single work set of 20s "part of the time," and "two sets of 10 to 15 reps part of the time." But he always squatted twice a week.

Now for some of what Peary had to say when he instructed others in the use of his interpretation of **Course #1**. Here's the "Standard Squat Course" in his *Master Bodybuilding and Weight Gaining System*: two-arm press, two-arm curl, two-arm bench press, rowing exercise, barbell squat (or deep knee bend), two-arm (breathing) pullover, and abdominal sit-up, in that order. (In a later recommendation he added a calf exercise.) That's very similar to my *Standard* version of **Course #1**, although I've substituted a couple of exercises, which I believe makes the routine even better.

He recognized that he had a personal bias towards the regular form of the squat. In his own words he wrote, "Possibly I'm rather partial to the squat because it did so much for me." But he noted that some people preferred the deadlift, the hip-belt squat, or the magic circle squat.

Peary recommended abbreviated versions for trainees who are short of time, or who can't progress on the standard version. This is the format he used, and it's what I term *Abridged*.

On depth of squatting, Peary recommended to the position where the top of the upper thighs is parallel to the floor, or just a little below that—but not all the way down.

Generally, Peary recommended the flat-footed squat, but he wasn't averse to a block as much as two inches thick being put under the heels for trainees whose leverages produce excessive forward lean. I used a board about one-inch thick under my heels for most of my 20-rep squats. It was the only way I could get down to parallel without leaning forward excessively and my lower back rounding. But the repercussions were knee irritation and injury. I don't recommend heel elevation. Instead, for bodybuilders not well suited to the traditional barbell squat, I prefer specific alternative exercises.

Although the magic circle squat is a possible alternative, and one that Peary promoted, it's not a practical one today because the required equipment isn't readily available. The hip-belt squat is an alternative Peary let his readers know about. I recommend the hip-belt squat when it's performed with the technique that's explained in this book. But I don't recommend the freestyle hip-belt squat even when it's done flat-footed; and I especially don't recommend it if it's done with elevated heels. I also like the alternative of the parallel-grip deadlift, but that requires a special bar that wasn't readily available during Peary's day, so he didn't publicize that exercise.

One more time . . . performing each workout's linchpin exercise *AS SPECIFIED*—with correct technique, sufficient effort, and enough poundage progression— is *MANDATORY*. Without it, Course #1 doesn't exist.

Duration of *The Growth Phase*

Assuming that you properly apply **Course #1**, you should get at least three to four consecutive months of *The Growth Phase*. (*Properly apply* means, in summary, that you fully satisfy the components of recuperation every day, and you fully satisfy all the components of training—a schedule that's sufficiently abbreviated for you, comprised of exercises well suited to you, performed with correct exercise technique and sufficient intensity, and with gradually ever-greater exercise poundages.)

Especially the first time you use **Course #1** (particularly if you're well short of realizing your full genetic potential for muscle mass), you may be able to extend *The Growth Phase* to six consecutive months, or longer still. Relentlessly apply the "slow cooking gaining momentum."

Peary applied *The Growth Phase* of his interpretation of an *Abridged* schedule for a much longer period than my general recommendation, albeit he mixed in "two sets of 10 to 15 reps part of the time" for the squat instead of a single work set of 20. (But perhaps he had some weeks when he backed off a bit, for some respite, to gather himself for his next dose of growth. In his later writings, Peary urged his readers to be conservative with their rate of progress.)

I recommend that you repeat **Course #1** for a full cycle once every 12 months or so, for a few consecutive years, rather than have a single extremely long period on it. Here are the three principle benefits of the recommended approach:

a) You have the opportunities—between periods on **Course #1**—to reduce your body fat and prevent excessive accumulation of it.

b) You can use other premier routines between periods on **Course #1**, to enable you to develop balanced strength and musculature throughout your physique.

c) You're less likely to experience the monotony that commonly occurs when the same format is sustained for a very long period. Monotony usually diminishes enthusiasm for working out, and undermines progress or even prohibits it.

CALL TO ARMS!

Even the very best training know-how is worthless unless it's fused with dedication to proper implementation.

Dedication includes *discipline*. Discipline means doing what needs to be done with consistency and perseverance.

If it's time to train, then train you must regardless of the weather, what's on TV, or whatever other potential distraction there may be. Make exercise a priority. But never bemoan the discipline that must accompany serious training. It's a privilege to be able to train.

And never bemoan the discipline that must be applied to your nutrition, sleep and rest in general. To have the opportunity to apply this discipline is a blessing.

Make each day count, and make each week a perfect example of training and recuperation. In other words, properly apply **Course #1**—week after week, and month after month.

Course #1 is worth your very best effort.

About the author

Born in 1958, in Stockton-on-Tees, England, I've had an almost lifelong appreciation of muscle and might. I started resistance training at age 14, when I got a set of chest expanders as a Christmas present. In 1973, at age 15, I started weight training, in a small "dungeon" gym at a local community center. That den became the focal point of my life until I left home in 1978 to go to college in Liverpool. Muscles were more important than everything else in my life. School work, social activities, and sport all played second fiddle to my quest to build a great physique.

Despite the 100% commitment, my initial gains were only very modest. After getting more "serious" about my training—namely, increasing its volume, frequency and intensity—progress came to a halt. Then started my fulsome appreciation of "hard gaining." Despite years of unrelenting total commitment to bodybuilding, the great physique that was promised didn't develop. I learned through great frustration that there was a lot more accounting for bodybuilding success than effort and dedication.

I gradually learned about the critical role of genetic factors, the need to use training routines appropriate to the individual, and the necessity of not imitating the training methods used by champion bodybuilders who have tremendous genetic advantages, and drug assistance.

Learning important truths about bodybuilding motivated me to share them with others. I wrote my first article while at college, and had it published by Peary Rader in *Iron Man* (the June-July 1981 issue). In addition to supplying further articles for *Iron Man*, I started writing for other bodybuilding magazines.

I graduated in 1982, but was unable to find a teaching post in England. I sought employment overseas. In January 1983 I was appointed at an international school in Nicosia, Cyprus. I stayed until summer 1984. Then I left due to an opportunity to visit the Hawaiian island of Molokai. I lived there for almost a year, then returned to Cyprus. Shortly afterwards, I married Maro, a Cypriot I'd known since my first stay on the Mediterranean island, and I settled in Cyprus.

In 1989 I founded CS Publishing and started a magazine called *THE HARDGAINER* (later changed to *HARDGAINER*). I finished *BRAWN* in 1991. In 1993 I gave up classroom teaching, and thereafter worked solely for CS Publishing. I completed *THE INSIDER'S TELL-ALL HANDBOOK ON WEIGHT-TRAINING TECHNIQUE* in 1996, and *BEYOND BRAWN* in 1998. (The three aforementioned books are now in their third editions.) In 2004 I retired *HARDGAINER*. I finished *BUILD MUSCLE, LOSE FAT, LOOK GREAT* in 2005, and in 2011 I started on the *New BRAWN Series*.

For much of my youth, my dream of becoming a professional, competitive bodybuilder ruled my life. But my lack of freaky genetics for bodybuilding, and my unwillingness to take bodybuilding drugs, ensured that I couldn't realize that dream. That failure was probably the single biggest disappointment of my youth. (But that I didn't get into drugs was a huge success.)

When I became a full-time writer and publisher of bodybuilding instruction, it was initially a substitute for not being a professional, competitive bodybuilder myself; but, with time, my passion for writing and publishing became as intense as my passion for my own bodybuilding during my youth. I ended up earning my living from bodybuilding, but not in the manner I had envisioned.

– Stuart McRobert

My other publications

Each of my other publications complements what this book teaches. You may want to read some of them for additional instruction and information to help you to reach your bodybuilding goals.

There are four other major bodybuilding books:
BRAWN
BEYOND BRAWN
BUILD MUSCLE, LOSE FAT, LOOK GREAT
THE INSIDER'S TELL-ALL HANDBOOK ON WEIGHT-TRAINING TECHNIQUE

And there are two supplementary publications:
HARDGAINER magazine
THE MUSCLE & MIGHT TRAINING TRACKER

The major bodybuilding books are available through some online retailers, and some bookstores; but the supplementary publications are available only from Cyprus—please visit www.hardgainer.com.

BRAWN

BRAWN is the classic book that started a training revolution. *BRAWN* focuses on genetic realities, appropriate role models, and most of the ins and outs of successful training. It's especially strong in the philosophical underpinning behind rational training. It also details how the genetically blessed are gifted, and shows why conventional training is so unproductive for typical people. *BRAWN* is now in a 230-page, third edition.

"*BRAWN* bowled me over. It's an exceptional nuts and bolts compilation of productive training practices; so exceptional, in fact, that it's avant-garde."
   – *Jan Dellinger*
   York Barbell Company, USA

"Are you tired of all the look-alike bodybuilding books? Are you tired of buying little more than a collection of photos of bodybuilding superstars and a pile of routines that will never work for the average person? Here's something different.
"If you thought Arnold Schwarzenegger put Graz, Austria on the bodybuilding map, how about Stuart McRobert and Nicosia, Cyprus? Imagine, one man, on a Mediterranean island, who has the audacity to directly challenge most contemporary bodybuilding advice. Instead of being yet another me-too bodybuilding book, McRobert's *BRAWN* is unique: Its tone is serious, its manner evangelical, but most important, its focus is on things that actually work for the average trainee. 'Drugs are evil and the scourge of bodybuilding,' says McRobert, in effect, 'and forget about Mr. O-type training—it just won't work for most people. I'll tell you about some things that do work.'"
   – *Randall J. Strossen, Ph.D.*
   Publisher of Milo, California, USA

"*BRAWN* has no hype, no bull, and no commercial messages. It's the real thing."
   – *Dr. Ken E. Leistner*
   Co-founder of Iron Island Gym, New York, USA

BRAWN costs $19.95.

BEYOND BRAWN

BEYOND BRAWN is 512 pages of information about every facet of bodybuilding, and weight training in general. Now in a third edition. This book is not just for novices. It can save you years of wasted toil regardless of your level of training experience. It will propel you into the detailed, practical know-how needed to turn you into an expertly informed bodybuilder or strength trainee. *BEYOND BRAWN* will take you right "inside" weight training, to study the practical reality of applying knowledge. It's not a theoretical treatise, or a pack of pseudo-scientific hokum.

"*BEYOND BRAWN* is the most comprehensive, helpful and honest book on natural strength training today. With great care and in extraordinary detail this book covers every training-related topic you can imagine, and without any hype."
– *Bob Whelan, MS, MS, CSCS, President, Whelan Strength Training, Washington, DC, USA*

"*BEYOND BRAWN* is the bible of rational strength training . . . Page after page is jam-packed with practical, real-world training information that you just cannot find anywhere else . . . This book has my highest endorsement—it's without a doubt the very best book on strength training I've ever read."
– *Kevin R. Fontaine, Ph.D., Assistant Professor of Medicine, Johns Hopkins University School of Medicine*

"For bodybuilding instruction, *BEYOND BRAWN* is par excellence, featuring an unprecedented depth of practical, relevant and readily applicable training information. Even more than that, the book is a training partner, companion, friend, and labor of love. A truly exceptional book!"
– *Jan Dellinger, York Barbell Company, USA*

My deadlift cycle that culminates in 400 pounds for 20 reps is detailed in Chapter 17 of this book.

BEYOND BRAWN costs $24.95.

Table of contents

Introduction *8*
How this book will help you *10*

SECTION 1: Establishing a secure foundation
1. Setting the scene for building muscle and might *21*
2. General philosophy for outstanding development *47*
3. All-time #1 practical priorities *63*
4. Expectations—how much muscle and might you can expect *75*
5. How to plan your growth *99*
6. Where to train, and the equipment you need *117*

SECTION 2: How to train
7. How to set up your training cycles for big returns *139*
8. How to achieve your fastest gains *167*
9. Hard work—the biggest test of training character *171*
10. Exercise selection and technique *189*
11. How to perform your reps *223*
12. How to design your own training programs *233*
13. How to personalize your training programs *255*
14. How to avoid the plague of overtraining *283*
15. How to milk your training cycles dry of gains *297*
16. Twenty-three extras for maximizing training productivity *305*
     Summary of how to ensure a successful training cycle *332*
     What if you're an extreme hard gainer? *333*

SECTION 3: Special issues

17.   A real-life training cycle for you to learn from *337*
18.   How a training nightmare was silenced *355*
19.   How to never let your age hold back your training *391*
20.   Your how-to of practical bodybuilding nutrition *401*
21.   Additional important training information *443*
22.   Beyond the exterior *459*
23.   How to get a grip on your life, and put all that you've learned from this book into action, now! *465*
    Postscript: Did you deliver? 476

About the author *479*
Index *487*

BUILD MUSCLE, LOSE FAT, LOOK GREAT

With 640 pages and nearly 400 photos, this book has an extraordinary quality and quantity of instruction and information, most of it additional to what's in *BEYOND BRAWN*. This guide is for men and women of all ages, and it's for you if you're a beginner or even if you have many years of training experience.

About 200 pages of this book (Chapter 12) are devoted to exercise technique, but that still leaves over 400 pages to cover other practical, usable information on bodybuilding and related topics.

"Stuart's authoritative book is crammed with responsible, safe, and highly effective instruction. It has my unreserved, professional endorsement."
  – Dr. Gregory Steiner, DC, MA, Allen, Texas, USA

"A brilliant book! Follow *The Program* developed by Stuart and you'll reach your potential for strength, muscle mass, fitness, and health."
  – Richard Winett, Ph.D.
    A professor at Virginia Tech, USA, publisher of Master Trainer, and award-winning health researcher

"Utterly complete, a book for men and women who want to 'be in shape,' or to compete at the highest level. All the required information is here."
  – Kathy Leistner, BA, MA, MS
    Exercise physiologist, past competitor at national and world powerlifting championships, and a former Ms. California, USA

"Use this unique book as your own expert personal trainer. It's packed with wise advice."
  – Rachael E. Picone, MS
    Exercise physiologist, speaker, and author, from New Jersey, USA

BUILD MUSCLE, LOSE FAT, LOOK GREAT costs $34.95.

The book's table of contents follows on the next page.

Table of contents for
BUILD MUSCLE, LOSE FAT, LOOK GREAT

Introduction *1*
Four Preliminaries *4*

PART 1: The Foundation
1.   Of first importance *13*
2.   How to get training immediately *17*
3.   The truth on age and exercise *71*
4.   How to optimize your recuperative powers *75*
5.   How to lose body fat *97*
6.   Physical restrictions, and their correction or management *105*
7.   Gym savvy, where to train, and gym conduct *123*

PART 2: How to Train
8.   The essential terminology of training *137*
9.   Cardio training *159*
10. How to avoid injuries *173*
11. Rep speed and control *189*
12. How to master exercise technique *193*
13. How to handle weights between exercises *403*
14. Seven extras for effective workouts *409*
15. How progressive resistance can help or hinder progress *417*
16. How to optimize your exercise selection from the gang of eight *423*
17. *The Program* *441*
18. Call to arms! *497*
19. Beyond *The Program* *501*

PART 3: Supplementary Material
20. Forewarned is forearmed *515*
21. What scientific studies really mean to you *523*
22. Burning issues *527*
23. A primer on anatomy *531*
24. The lexicon of muscle-building, and training *543*

About the author *611*
Resources *614*
Index *621*

THE INSIDER'S TELL-ALL HANDBOOK ON WEIGHT-TRAINING TECHNIQUE

To benefit from exercise, you must avoid injuries, and train consistently and effectively. But if you don't use correct exercise technique, you'll get injured frequently, and you'll be unable to train consistently and effectively using the best exercises. With 300 pages and 363 photographs, this book is thorough. Follow its guidance and become your own expert personal trainer on exercise technique. This guide is for men and women of all ages and levels of training experience. This third edition incorporates Chapter 12 of *BUILD MUSCLE, LOSE FAT, LOOK GREAT,* along with additional exercises and other information.

"I'm a chiropractor and acupuncturist with over 25 years of training experience. And I've provided many people with personal training. Stuart's books are unique—authoritative, thorough, clear, and inspirational. And no one covers exercise technique with the care, precision and attention to safety that he does. Without any reservation, I recommend Stuart's books to everyone who lifts weights."
  – *Dr. Gregory Steiner, DC, MA, Allen, Texas, USA*

"I've been lifting weights most of my life. I'm no novice. I was blown away when I realized, after reading your book, how much I didn't know about proper exercise form. I can't recommend this book enough."
  – *John Leschinski, Connell, Washington, USA*

THE INSIDER'S TELL-ALL HANDBOOK ON WEIGHT-TRAINING TECHNIQUE COSTS $19.95.

Table of contents

Introduction   *10*

PART 1
  How to train safely   *14*
  Rep speed and control   *28*
  The four main hand grips   *30*
  A primer on anatomy   *32*

PART 2
How to master exercise technique   *46*
  1. Back extension   *basic back extension*   *54*
                           45-degree back extension   *57*
                           spinal extension   *57*
                           machine back extension   *58*
  2. Bench press   *barbell bench press*   *60*
                           dumbbell bench press   *68*
                           close-grip bench press   *72*
                           incline barbell bench press   *76*
                           incline dumbbell bench press   *80*
  3. Calf raise   *standing two-legged calf raise*   *84*
                           standing one-legged calf raise   *86*
  4. Chin-up (and pull-up)   *88*
  5. Crunch   *basic crunch*   *94*
                           modified basic crunch   *96*
                           machine crunch   *97*
                           reverse crunch   *98*
                           twisting crunch   *100*

6. Curl	seated dumbbell curl	104
	incline dumbbell curl	105
	barbell curl	106
	hammer curl	107
7. Deadlift	deadlift (basic, or conventional deadlift)	112
	parallel-grip deadlift	122
	partial deadlift	130
	sumo deadlift	134
8. Finger extension		136
9. Hand-gripper work	torsion-spring gripper	139
	Ivanko super gripper	141
10. Lateral raise	dumbbell lateral raise	144
	machine lateral raise	145
11. Leg curl		146
12. Leg press		150
13. L-fly		156
14. Neck work	manual resistance neck work	161
	four-way neck machine	162
15. Parallel bar dip		164
16. Press	seated barbell press	168
	seated dumbbell press	172
17. Pulldown		176
18. Pullover	machine pullover	180
	breathing pullover	184
19. Pushdown		186
20. Rotary torso		188
21. Row	one-arm dumbbell row	190
	cable row	192
	seated machine row	196
	prone low-incline dumbbell row	197
22. Shrug		198
23. Side bend	dumbbell side bend	203
	pulley side bend	205
24. Squat	squat (conventional or back squat)	212
	front squat	230
	ball squat	240
	hip-belt squat	244
25. Timed hold		250

Supplementary exercises
26. Grip machine training	254
27. Lever bar work	256
28. Overhead lockout	258
29. Pinch-grip lifting	262
30. Rader chest pull	266
31. Wrist roller training	268

PART 3
How to handle weights between exercises	274
How to compose exercise technique checklists	280
Video recordings: the acid test of correct exercise technique	282
How to become flexible	288
About the author	308

HARDGAINER magazine

From July 1989 until its retirement in early 2004 there were 89 issues of *HARDGAINER*. It provided more result-producing advice for bodybuilders and strength trainees than was available in any other magazine. It was free of mainstream hokum, but crammed with practical advice, and wisdom. It spoke to the typical individual. But average potential doesn't have to mean average achievements. In fact, an impressive physique and a terrific level of strength are well within your reach. They key, though, is in the right approach. That's what *HARDGAINER* was about. Fresh information, and the expertise and experiences of a range of contributors can be found in each issue. And there's plenty of grassroots material, to show you the ins and outs of the practical reality of training.

The content of *HARDGAINER* doesn't date. The back issues represent a wealth of experience and advice. *HARDGAINER* includes such features as:

Inspirational pieces on developing the right training philosophy for you.

Sample workouts for bodybuilders, powerlifters, and strength trainees.

Advice for new, intermediate, and advanced trainees.

Guidance on the psychology of training.

Exercise equipment; and training in home gyms, and commercial gyms.

"From the Grassroots" articles, success stories, and readers' letters.

Questions and answers on all aspects of training and related topics.

Guidance and tips on nutrition, and recuperation in general.

Guidance on the treatment and prevention of injuries.

And Stuart edited each issue, and contributed to each one, too.

While most of the first 44 issues are in photocopy format, all the others are in original format although some of them will be in that format for a limited period only. All the back issues are available, however. The contents of each issue are listed at www.hardgainer.com.

MUSCLE & MIGHT TRAINING TRACKER

This 136-page workbook contains everything you need to track your progress—day by day, week by week, month by month, year by year.

A training journal is indispensable for keeping you on track for training success. No matter where you are now—180-pound squat or 500, 13-inch arms or 17, 135-pound bench press or 350—the systematic organization and focus upon achieving goals that a training journal enforces, will help you to improve your physique steadily and consistently. While most trainees are aware of the potential value of a training log, few actually keep one; and that's one of the major reasons why they make minimal or no progress.

There are sample filled-out log pages, and then many detailed blank log pages. The pages track not only the specifics of your weight training—exercises, set-up details, sets and reps, poundages, and a comments area for each workout—but also nutrition, sleep, and body composition.

As simple as it is to use a training log, don't underestimate the critical role it can play in helping you to maximize your training productivity. One training log will track your progress for at least 24 months. And this log is built for the job it's designed to do. For example, its robust paper provides the strength to withstand heavy use, and the spiral binding enables the book to open flat for ease of use when entering data. This is no ordinary training diary.

THE MUSCLE & MIGHT TRAINING TRACKER costs $19.95.

Index

A

Abbreviated training
    necessity of, 21, 180
Abridged schedules, 187–188
Active Release Techniques®, 40
Anabolic steroids, 15
Anatomy, 98–106
    charts, 100–101
    definition, 97
Appetite and training, 70

B

Beginners, recommendation, 181
Belt
    lifting, 56
    weight, 56, 141
Berry, Mark, 12
Breath counting, 196–197
Breath holding, 57
Breathing
    forced, 196–197
    for linchpin exercises, 57
"Breathing squats," 197
Bulking-trimming, 27

C

Calf machine shrug, 155
Calf work, health benefits, 119
Calibrated weight plates, 48
Caloric intake, 68–70
Cambered squat bar, 27, 35, 161, 201
Camcorder, 63, 117
Chalk, 52, 53
Champion bodybuilders
    problems with, 15
Complementary exercises, 182–183
Compound exercises, 181
Conventional bodybuilding methods
    problems with, 14

D

Dedication, 31, 203
Douglass, James. E., 27

E

Easy gainers, 18
Economics and *Course #1*, 16

Eells, Roger, 197
Exercise equipment, safety, 159, 164
Exercise selection/suitability, 37
Exercise technique
    definition, 96
    importance of, 38
Exercise Technique, The, 94–175
    Bench press, 108–117
        barbell bench press, 108–111
        dumbbell bench press, 112–114
        incline bench press, 116–117
    Breathing pullover, 118
    Calf raise, 119–121
        standing two-legged calf raise, 120
        standing one-legged calf raise, 121
    Chin-up and pull-up, 122–123
    Crunch, 124–127
        basic crunch, 125
        modified basic crunch, 126
        machine crunch, 126
        reverse crunch, 127
    Curl, 128–130
        barbell curl, 130
        hammer curl, 130
        incline dumbbell curl, 129
        seated dumbbell curl, 129
    Deadlift, 131–139
        parallel-grip deadlift, 132–137
        partial deadlift, 138–139
    Parallel bar dip, 140–141
    Press, 142–145
        seated barbell press, 142–143
        seated dumbbell press, 144–145
    Pulldown, 146–147
    Rader chest pull, 148
    Row, 149–153
        cable row, 150–152
        prone low-incline dumbbell row, 153
        one-arm dumbbell row, 149
        seated machine row, 152–153
    Shrug, 154–155
    Side bend, 156–157
        dumbbell side bend, 156
        pulley side bend, 157
    Squat, 158–173
        barbell squat, 161–169
        hip-belt squat, 170–173
    Thick-bar hold, 174–175
Expanded schedules, 185

F

Flexibility
    importance of, 39
    routine, 84–93
Footwear, 58
Fat
    dietary, 71
    body, 27, 82
Fiber, dietary, 71–72
Food supplements, 75–76
Forced reps, 43, 184
Foundation Phase, The, 80–93

G

Gains, rate of, 26–27
Genetics, 17
Gerard, Al, 24
Grip aids, 52, 53
Grip strength, 52
Grips, four main, 107
Growth Phase, The, 176–203
Gyms, suitability of, 35

H

Hard gainers, 18–19
Health, 14, 79
Heels and squatting motions, 173
Hindrances, physical, 40
Hip-belt squat
    as linchpin exercise, 23, 182
    advantages, 24
    suitability of, 37, 182
    technique, 170–173
Hip flexors, and ab work, 125
Hise, Joseph, C., 12
History of *Course #1*, 12

I

Individual variation, 13, 30, 40, 181, 190
Iron Man, 12, 21, 30, 201, 202
Intensifiers, 43
Isolation exercises, 181

L

Linchpin exercises
    alternatives, 22–25
    breathing for, 57, 196–197

definition, 22
equipment for, 36
intensity of, 200
set performance of, 198–199
    See also Parallel-grip deadlift; Squat, barbell;
        Squat, hip-belt
Little gems, 49, 202
Logbook, training, 54

M

Machinery, 36
Magic circle, 27, 202
McRobert, Stuart
    composition of gain, 19
    illustration of *Course #1*, 193
    injury recovery, 40
    success summary, 13
Meal planning, 72–73
Meal preparation, 73–74
Milk, 72
Mirrors, 63
Muscle growth quantity, 26–27

N

Negative reps, 43, 184
Nutrition, 68–76
    caloric intake, 68–70
    fat, 71
    fiber, 71–72
    food quantity variation, 73
    food supplements, 75–76
    meal planning, 72–73
    meal preparation, 73–74
    milk, 72
    post-workout nutrition, 75
    pre-workout nutrition, 75
    protein, 70–71
    water, 74–75

P

Parallel-grip deadlift
    as linchpin exercise, 23, 182
    advantages, 24
    suitability of, 37, 182
    technique, 132–137
Park, Reg, 17, 18
Partner, training, 55

Poundage increments, small, 49, 50, 51, 202
Poundage progression, 194–195
Procedures, The, 32–65
Program design, 182–192
Progression in the linchpin exercises, 195
Protein, 70–71

R

Rader, Peary
   alternatives to the barbell squat, 27
   chest pull, 148
   composition of gains, 19
   Master Bodybuilding and Weight-Gaining System
      21, 201, 202
   and origins of *Course #1*, 12
   his own training and advice, 201–202
   preferred style of squatting, 197
   promotion of *Course #1*, 21
   his suitability for the barbell squat, 30, 200–202
   small increments, 49, 202
   squat achievement, 45
Recuperation, importance, 34
Recuperation, The, 66–79
Rep counting and breath holding, 196–197
Rep speed, 41
Rest, general, 79
Rest-pause reps, explanation, 25
Revelations, The, 10–31
Rosin, 52, 53

S

Safety equipment, 159, 164
Scheduling recommendations, 191–192
Schwarzenegger, Arnold, 15, 18
Shoulder harness, 141

Shrug bar, 23, 24, 35, 132
Sickness, 64
Sleep, 76–79
Smith machine squat, 169
Spotting, 54
Squat
   alternatives, 23
   magic of, 22
   suitability for, 37, 182
   technique, 158–173
      barbell squat, 161–169
      hip-belt squat, 170–173
   See also Rader, Peary
Standard schedules, 186–187
Strength, building, 45, 46–47, 49, 50, 51
   caveat, 29
Supplements, food, 75–76

T

Thick bar, 174
Training frequency options, 189–190
Training intensity, 42, 43, 200
   cycling, 44
Training logbook, 54
Training partner, 55
Trap bar, 23, 24, 35, 132
Trimming-building, 27

W

Warming up
   general, 61
   specific, 62
Water intake, 63, 74–75
Women and *Course #1*, 14

Also by Stuart McRobert

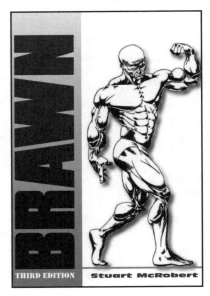

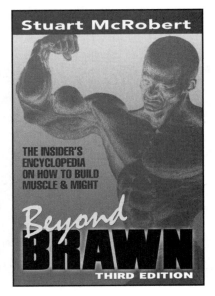

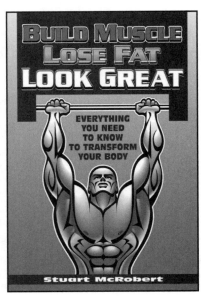